Edna Umel

6415   St.   Catherines St

Van.   V5W 3G9

321- 6302   or 760-1871

The clinical scenarios described in this book are entirely fictional. No resemblance to real people or actual cases is intended.

Every effort was made to ensure the accuracy of the material presented in this book at the time of publication.

Given that policies, procedures, and instructions can change at any time, candidates should always read and follow directions provided by the regulatory authority, the presiding officer, and the instructions contained in the Canadian Registered Nurse Examination.

Candidates use the information, materials, and suggestions in this book at their own risk. Neither the Canadian Nurses Association nor Assessment Strategies Inc. assumes any responsibility for candidates' performance on the Canadian Registered Nurse Examination.

ISBN 1-55119-172-5. 3RD EDITION, 2000
(ISBN 1-55119-132-6. 2ND EDITION, 1995)
(ISBN 0-88879-036-8. 1ST EDITION, 1992)

Printed in Canada

Table of Contents

Preface

The Canadian Nurses Association (CNA) is pleased to introduce the 3rd edition of the *Canadian RN Exam Prep Guide*. By all accounts the previous two editions have been a great success. We are particularly proud to be launching this edition, which includes a CD-ROM version of the Practice Exam. We believe that this added feature, along with the other enhancements we have incorporated, will make this the most useful guide yet.

As the nursing profession in Canada continues to evolve, so must the RN Exam which measures the readiness of nursing students to deliver safe and effective nursing care to the public. This new edition of the *Prep Guide* has been developed to help students prepare for the revised RN Exam, to be first written in June 2000. The RN Exam will continue to be evaluated annually to reaffirm that the competencies and the guidelines for examination development reflect what is expected of an entry-level registered nurse beginning to practise.

This is an exciting time for the writers of the RN Exam; it's also an exciting and challenging time for nurses across Canada. The continual review of the RN Exam and the production of the *Prep Guide* are two of the ways CNA contributes to the growth of the nursing profession.

On behalf of CNA, I'd like to thank the many registered nurses who collaborated with us to produce this edition of the *Prep Guide*. I also want to wish you success in writing the Exam and in your nursing career.

Mary Ellen Jeans

Mary Ellen Jeans, RN, PhD
Executive Director
CNA

Acknowledgments

The following people generously gave their time and expertise to the creation of *The Canadian RN Exam Prep Guide* (3rd ed.).

Exam Review Panel

This panel consisted of nine nurses from different locations and work settings in Canada. They reviewed the content of the Practice Exam and rationales—independently and as a group—to ensure the quality of these important *Prep Guide* components.

Odette Arseneau
Université de Moncton
Campus de Shippigan-Site Bathurst
Bathurst, New Brunswick

Suzanne Bertrand
Hôpital Régional de Sudbury SJHC
Sudbury, Ontario

Rinette Côté
Université de Moncton, Campus d'Edmunston
Edmunston, Nouveau-Brunswick

Mary S. Elliott
Humber College of Applied Arts and Technology
Etobicoke, Ontario

Janice Henty
George Brown College, Faculty of Nursing
Toronto, Ontario

Sonia Jablonski-Praznik
Red River College
Winnipeg, Manitoba

Charlotte L'Heureux-Lemieux
Université de Moncton
Campus de Shippigan-Site Bathurst
Bathurst, New Brunswick

Maxine Quinlan-Freeman
Lambton College
Sarnia, Ontario

Lois N. Tessier
University of Manitoba/RRC joint BN Program
Red River College
Winnipeg, Manitoba

Nurse Item Writers

The following nurses participated in item-writing sessions conducted in 1999, at which questions and rationales were developed for use on the Practice Exam.

Beverly A. Clark
University of Manitoba
Brandon, Manitoba

Rinette Côté
Université de Moncton, Campus d'Edmunston
Edmunston, New Brunswick

Gwennet Culley
St. Michael's Hospital/Seneca College
Toronto, Ontario

Nancy Fleming
Confederation College
Thunder Bay, Ontario

Catherine Harrop
University of Calgary/Mount Royal College
Canmore, Alberta

Lynda M. Haug
Misericordia Hospital
Edmonton, Alberta

Marilynne Hogg
Health Sciences Centre
Winnipeg, Manitoba

Susan MacLeay
Confederation College
Thunder Bay, Ontario

France Marquis
Université de Moncton, Campus d'Edmunston
Edmunston, New Brunswick

Elaine McKiel
University of Calgary
Calgary, Alberta

Chantal Morin
La Cité collégiale
Ottawa, Ontario

Susan Mussell
Women's Hospital, Health Sciences Centre
Winnipeg, Manitoba

Anita Pelletier
Université Laurentienne
Sudbury, Ontario

Céline Pelletier
Stanton Regional Hospital
Yellowknife, Northwest Territories

Sharon Ronaldson
Langara College
Vancouver, British Columbia

Marie St-Onge
Université Laurentienne
Sudbury, Ontario

Peri Venkatesh
University of Manitoba
Winnipeg, Manitoba

Penelope Vernon
George Brown College, Faculty of Nursing
Toronto, Ontario

Gail E. Watson
Nanaimo Regional General Hospital
Nanaimo, British Columbia

Canadian Nurses Association (CNA) and Assessment Strategies Inc. (ASI) Staff

A number of CNA and ASI staff members contributed, in different ways, to the creation of *The Canadian RN Exam Prep Guide* (3rd ed.). These people included those who were responsible for planning and managing all of the activities related to the development of the *Prep Guide*, along with several individuals who were asked to assist with specific aspects of the project.

CNA and ASI Staff Contributors

Heather Broughton, Association Editor, CNA
Martine Devaux, Translator/Reviser, CNA
Lucie Hardy, Executive Assistant, ASI
Brenda Julien-Pinsent,
 Senior Program Assistant, ASI
Johanne Killeen, Director,
 Assessment Programs, ASI
Don Laberge, Program Assistant, ASI
Yves Lafortune, Consultant, ASI
Karin Noel, Coordinator,
 Information Systems, ASI
Diane St-Pierre, Consultant, ASI
Ondina Love, Marketing/Sponsor Manager, CNA
Nathalie Lalonde, Layout Artist, CNA

Chapter 1
Using this guide

Introduction

The *Canadian RN Exam Prep Guide* (3rd ed.) has been developed by the Canadian Nurses Association's (CNA) subsidiary testing agency, Assessment Strategies Inc. The purpose of the *Prep Guide* is to assist candidates who will be writing the Canadian Registered Nurse Examination (RN Exam). This third edition of the *Prep Guide* is designed specifically for those candidates who plan to write the RN Exam in June 2000 or later.

The current version of the RN Exam is offered as a paper and pencil examination. For your benefit, however, we have included a CD-ROM in this third edition of the *Prep Guide*. The CD-ROM provides you with the opportunity to prepare on your computer for taking the RN Exam. You can choose between two approaches. One approach allows you to take the Practice Exam under the same condition as the actual exam (i.e., testing mode). The other approach, which is referred to as the feedback mode, allows you to receive immediate feedback following your response to a question. Both approaches give you a summary of your total performance at the end of your session.

Success on the RN Exam depends on two main factors: (1) your knowledge of nursing principles and content, and (2) your ability to apply this knowledge, in the context of specific health care scenarios, on the RN Exam.

This guide can help you in both areas. Completing the *Prep Guide* Practice Exam will help you review and integrate the concepts you have learned in your nursing program; it will also help you assess your skill in applying that knowledge. The test instructions, test-taking strategies, question rationales, and sample answer sheets can be used to enhance your readiness to write the RN Exam. The CD-ROM addition to this edition should also prove beneficial. What better way to get ready than to gain practical experience by trying the practice questions in the *Prep Guide* and knowing what to expect on the RN Exam!

The *Prep Guide* consists of several chapters designed to help you with different aspects of your preparation. In this chapter, you will learn the best way to use the *Prep Guide* and the CD-ROM enclosure, given your individual needs and the amount of time you have to prepare for the RN Exam. Chapter 2 provides you with background information on the development, organization, and format of the RN Exam. Chapter 3 contains a variety of general test-taking strategies, as well as specific strategies for answering multiple-choice questions. The Practice Exam is presented in Chapter 4 as well as on the CD-ROM. Chapter 5 explains how to use the answer keys to score the Practice Exam, and describes how the actual RN Exam is scored.

After checking your score on the Practice Exam against a score interpretation scale, you may wish to develop a Performance Profile—a self-evaluation of your strengths and weaknesses. Chapter 6 shows you how to create your Performance Profile. This profile is created automatically when you take the Practice Exam on the CD-ROM. The rationales for each option in the Practice Exam are found in Chapter 7 and are presented to you when you work with the CD-ROM in the feedback mode.

The Bibliography lists all the references cited in the question rationales. Appendix A presents the competencies that make up the content domain for the RN Exam. Addresses of the provincial and territorial regulatory authorities are provided in Appendix B, and Appendix C contains a list of common abbreviations that appear on the RN Exam. At the end of the *Prep Guide*, you will find two blank answer sheets for the Practice Exam, a blank tally sheet to create your Performance Profile, and a Satisfaction Survey. Your opinion is important to us and we encourage you to send us your feedback so we may improve future editions of *The Canadian RN Exam Prep Guide*.

Finally, on the inside back cover, your copy of the CD-ROM is enclosed.

Before You Begin...

The *Prep Guide* is designed to familiarize you with the format of the actual exam and to provide you with information on the content of the exam. The Practice Exam contained in this book and also on the CD-ROM is a simulation of an actual RN Exam. There are 260 questions in the Practice Exam (two exam books, each containing 130 questions).

The questions presented in the Practice Exam are typical of those you will see on the RN Exam. They represent common and predictable health situations of the population in those contexts or environments where nurses beginning to practise would work in a generalist role. As with the actual RN Exam, the questions on the Practice Exam have been developed and reviewed by nurses who represent a variety of nursing programs, different clinical backgrounds, and different regions of the country. Furthermore, the Practice Exam has been designed according to the specifications and guidelines outlined in the *Blueprint for the Canadian Registered Nurse Examination (1999)*, the document used to construct the actual RN Exam. Hence, although the Practice Exam is not identical to the RN Exam that you will write, both exams contain questions that measure specific competencies expected of nurses beginning to practise.

One of the most important features of the *Prep Guide* is that, for each question on the Practice Exam, rationales are provided to explain why the options are correct or incorrect. These rationales emphasize nursing concepts and principles that are essential for beginning practitioners. For example, although the pharmacology questions and the communication questions on the *Prep Guide* Practice Exam are different from those on the actual exam, the general

principles and concepts being tested are the same, because the questions are developed from the same set of competencies. Thus, by using the Practice Exam to review and reinforce the principles of safe administration of medication and therapeutic communication, you will be better prepared to answer these types of questions on the RN Exam.

It is important to note that, although your score on the Practice Exam can give you some indication of how prepared you are for the RN Exam, the *Prep Guide* is only one aid to promoting your success. The *Prep Guide* should be used to supplement and reinforce the knowledge and skills taught in your educational program.

Each question on the *Prep Guide* Practice Exam is supported by two references. Most of these references have been published within the past five years. The purpose of the references is twofold: to indicate that the correct answer within each of the questions has authoritative support from at least two experts in the field; and to provide you with a source for further reading and review. Every attempt has been made to use references that are up-to-date, accessible, and accepted within the nursing community. If you are unable to locate the specific references cited in the Bibliography, there are many other equally sound nursing texts that provide support for the questions in the Practice Exam.

Methods of Using the Prep Guide

The *Prep Guide*, including the CD-ROM, can be used in different ways, depending on your particular needs and the amount of time you have before you write the RN Exam. The three methods suggested below are not independent, but can actually be used successively as part of a comprehensive study plan. Each method should be preceded by a review of Chapters 1, 2, and 3 before advancing to Chapter 4, *Taking the Practice Exam*, or using the CD-ROM. The three methods differ in approach, based on the amount of time you have available before you write the RN Exam. They cover periods of several months prior, one month prior, and two weeks prior to the actual exam.

Method A: If You Have Several Months Before Writing the Exam

If you have several months before the exam, you may wish to write the complete Practice Exam under conditions that do not simulate the actual exam (e.g., do not be concerned with time limits; look ahead to a rationale to understand why a given answer is correct, before choosing your answer). Consider this process as a "dry run" to familiarize yourself with the *Prep Guide* and the format and layout of the exam. In using this approach, work question-by-question without using the answer sheets. Answer one question and immediately check whether you selected the correct answer. Then read the rationales for the correct answer and the incorrect options, to gain insight into what made you answer correct or incorrect.

On the CD-ROM this would correspond to the feedback mode where you receive immediate feedback on whether you responded correctly or incorrectly, and why. If you repeat a session on feedback mode, the order of the exam questions will be randomized each time.

This method will give you hands-on experience with multiple-choice questions, and help you identify any difficulties you may have with the multiple-choice format (e.g., not picking up on key words in the question, making unwarranted assumptions, and reading too much into questions). On page 23, you will find a Checklist of Common Test-Taking Errors that will help you determine if you have particular difficulties with multiple-choice questions that you can correct before writing the exam.

Since this method does not simulate actual exam conditions, we recommend that you do not calculate your total score or make any inferences based on how you do.

Method B: If You Have One Month Before Writing the Exam

If you have approximately one month before the exam, you will want to more closely simulate actual exam conditions, and still take advantage of a considerable amount of time in which to address any self-diagnosed weaknesses. With this method, complete the Practice Exam, either in its entirety or in discrete sections (e.g., a set of cases, a set of independent questions, or one exam book) before checking your answers against the answer key. Next, calculate your total score and interpret it according to the guidelines provided in Chapter 5. Then develop your Performance Profile, to identify your strengths and weaknesses.

The results of this self-diagnosis can then be used to identify gaps or deficiencies in your knowledge and skills. By knowing that you are weak in particular competence categories, for example, you can make your remaining study time more productive by concentrating on those specific areas. Studying for the RN Exam will also be made easier by consulting the reference books linked to specific topics in nursing. You will find these references cited in the rationales for each question, and listed in full in the Bibliography.

If you use the CD-ROM version of the Practice Exam, you would be in the testing mode. However, you would not necessarily respect the time limits of the actual exam or complete an entire book in one sitting.

Method C: If You Have Two Weeks Before Writing the Exam

Method C is based upon the complete simulation of the actual exam. Follow the Practice Exam instructions precisely, time yourself, and use the answer sheets, as if you were actually writing the

RN Exam. You can still benefit from creating your Performance Profile as suggested in Method B. For the remaining study time, it may be most useful for you to concentrate on specific areas in which any weaknesses were identified. When using Method C, if you do not have time to obtain the references that correspond to your areas of weakness, you may prefer to concentrate on the rationales provided for each question in the Practice Exam.

Applying Method C on the CD-ROM corresponds to the testing mode. Here, as in the paper and pencil approach, you would respect all the administration guidelines (time limits, no reference materials, etc.). Your result and a Performance Profile will be generated automatically when you have completed the entire Practice Exam in the testing mode.

Chapter 2
Background on the RN Exam

Background on the RN Exam

Each Canadian provincial and territorial regulatory authority for nurses is responsible for ensuring that all entry-level registered nurses within its jurisdiction meet an acceptable level of competence before they begin to practise. This level of competence is measured partly by the Canadian Registered Nurse Examination administered by all provincial and territorial regulatory authorities, except in Québec.[1] This ensures a common standard that all nurses practising in these jurisdictions must meet.

The Canadian Nurses Association, through Assessment Strategies Inc., has been developing the RN Exam since 1970. (Before that, jurisdictions made their own arrangements for testing, and most used exams developed in the United States.) Originally, each exam book represented a discrete clinical area (e.g., medicine, surgery, pediatrics, etc.); since August 1980, however, the exam content has been integrated to make the exam comprehensive in nature. That is, the material from areas such as pharmacology, nutrition, growth and development, etc., is incorporated into a variety of health care situations that a nurse entering practice as a generalist is most likely to encounter.

In 1993, CNA introduced significant changes to the process used to develop the RN Exam. At that time, the process was changed from a norm-referenced approach to a *criterion-referenced* (C-R) approach. With the C-R approach, the RN Exam is developed to measure an explicitly defined content domain, which consists of the competencies expected of nurses beginning to practise. In 1998-99, a thorough review and updating of these competencies resulted in a new set of competencies which forms the basis of the June 2000 and later versions of the examination. These new competencies, and the guidelines and specifications that outline the way they are measured on the exam, are presented in the CNA publication *Blueprint for the Canadian Registered Nurse Examination* (1999).

As with the previous exams, the new version of the RN Exam is the end result of many test development activities that take place throughout a two-year period. Nurse educators, clinicians, and administrators from across Canada create and evaluate exam questions with assistance from Assessment Strategies Inc. test consultants who ensure that the RN Exam meets the *Blueprint* guidelines and specifications.

2

---

[1] The regulatory authorities impose eligibility criteria, such as the completion of an approved program of nursing education, which provide the added information required to decide on an individual's readiness to practise nursing.

What is Tested with the RN Exam

As mentioned on the previous page, the content and specifications for the RN Exam are described in the *Blueprint*. A Summary Chart that outlines the *Blueprint* specifications for exam development is presented on page 13 for your reference. And, in Appendix A, you will find the complete list of 183 competencies that make up the content domain for the RN Exam. Each question on the RN Exam is linked to one of these competencies. The sections below provide brief explanations of the variables and guidelines referred to in the Summary Chart.

Competencies

This first section of the Summary Chart shows that the set of competencies has been broken into two groups, and that each group receives a different weight on the RN Exam. The two groups were formed on the basis of a competency validation survey, in which nurses across Canada rated the competencies according to importance and frequency. Group 1 consists of the 54 competencies identified as *very important* for the safe and effective practice of entry-level registered nurses; these competencies form 45-50% of the exam. Group 2 consists of the 129 competencies identified as *important* for the safe and effective practice of entry-level registered nurses; these competencies form 50-55% of the exam. Note that the list of competencies in Appendix A also indicates to which of the two groups the competency has been assigned.

Structural Variables

The general structure and appearance of the RN Exam are governed by the following structural variables:

Examination Length and Format

The RN Exam consists of 240-260 multiple-choice questions.

Test Equating

To ensure the equivalency of different versions of the RN Exam (e.g., French and English versions, or same-language versions administered at different times), a predetermined set of questions, known as anchor items, will appear on all exam versions.

Item Presentation

Approximately half of the questions on the RN Exam are presented in a *case-based* format; i.e., a group of approximately five questions that are associated with a brief introductory text. The remainder of the exam consists of *independent questions*, which are stand-alone questions not directly associated with the cases or other questions on the exam.

Taxonomies: Cognitive and Affective Domains

Questions on the RN Exam measure candidates' knowledge and abilities in nursing content across different levels of the *cognitive* domain. The three levels of cognitive ability reflected in the RN Exam are: Knowledge/Comprehension, Application, and Critical Thinking. As well, because the competencies are defined in the *Blueprint* to include attitudes and judgment, certain questions on the exam are designed to measure aspects of the *affective* domain. The cognitive and affective domains are defined below.

The Cognitive Domain
Knowledge/Comprehension
This level refers to those mental abilities used when you recall and understand certain definitions, facts, or principles. For example, a sound base of nursing knowledge is required for you to know common side effects of a certain medication and to understand your client's physiological reactions to it. Knowledge/comprehension questions make up 25-30% of the RN Exam.

2

Application

This level refers to the ability to apply your knowledge in new or practical situations. For example, you would be using application skills when you incorporate principles of nutrition into a health-teaching plan for a newly diagnosed client with diabetes. Approximately half the questions on the RN Exam are at the application level.

Critical Thinking

This level refers to your ability to solve problems. This means formulating valid conclusions and making decisions about nursing care. For example, you have to use your critical thinking skills when prioritizing nursing interventions in a crisis situation. The critical thinking level of the cognitive domain is represented by 20-30% of the questions on the RN Exam.

The Affective Domain

The RN Exam is also designed to assess competencies that involve attributes such as attitudes and judgment, which do not fall strictly within the cognitive domain. For the RN Exam, the affective domain is defined to have three levels: (1) Receiving/Responding; (2) Valuing; and (3) Organization/Characterization. These levels address such areas as examination of personal values, interpersonal interactions with clients and colleagues, and identification of professional limits. Note that the three levels are not weighted individually; rather, an overall weight of 4-8% of the exam is assigned to questions from the affective domain.

Competency Framework

A framework was developed to identify and organize the competencies the RN Exam should assess. The resulting framework is reflective of a primary health care nursing model. The framework and definitions of the six framework categories are presented below. The number of competencies in each category is indicated in parentheses following the category name. The number of competencies in each category is not necessarily reflective of the importance each area of competency has in the practice of nursing.

Nurse-Client Relationship (15 competencies)

The nurse-client relationship is a relationship that is therapeutic and is established to meet the health needs of clients. The relationship is based on trust, respect, and knowledge, and involves interactions that are purposeful and focused on working with clients to maximize client-identified health status outcomes (Nurses Association of New Brunswick/l'Association des infirmières et infirmiers du Nouveau-Brunswick, 1995).

Health Promotion (31 competencies)

Health promotion is a focus of care motivated by the desire to enable clients to increase control over and improve their well-being, thereby actualizing client health potential. It includes encouraging healthy lifestyles, creating supportive environments for health, strengthening community action, reorienting health services, and building healthy public policy (Pender, 1996).

Illness/Injury Prevention (22 competencies)

Illness/injury prevention is a focus of care motivated by the desire to enable clients to avoid illness and injury. It includes risk factor reduction, screening and early detection of illness, communicable disease control, and environmental health and safety.

Curative/Supportive Care (69 competencies)

The focus of curative/supportive care is to help clients deal with responses associated with illness or health issues/problems, along with activities designed to support clients as they resolve their health problems or participate in palliative care (Ordre des infirmières et infirmiers du Québec, March 1996).

Rehabilitative Care (15 competencies)

The focus of rehabilitative care is to assist clients with a physical or psychosocial disabling injury or illness to achieve maximum functioning or independence. This includes counselling, support, retraining and education, and environmental modifications (Craven and Hirnle, 1996).

Professional Practice (31 competencies)

Each nurse is accountable to clients for practising within professional, legal, and ethical standards. This includes applying quality improvement principles, using evidence-based knowledge and critical thinking, establishing collaborative partnerships, coordinating care, monitoring practice, enhancing practice, and recognizing and acting on learning needs (College of Nurses of Ontario, 1996, and Canadian Nurses Association, 1993).

Contextual Variables

Client Type

For the purpose of the RN Exam, the client is defined as the individual, family, group, population, or community that accesses the services of the entry-level registered nurse.

Client Age and Gender

Specifications are provided for the age and gender of the clients described in the RN Exam. The use of these variables ensures that the clients described in the exam represent the demographic characteristics of the population encountered by the nurse beginning to practise. Client ages are categorized into four levels: Child & Adolescent (0-18 years); Adult (19-64 years); Older Adult (65-79 years) and Adult of Advanced Age (80+ years).

Client Culture

The RN Exam is designed to include questions representing the variety of cultural backgrounds encountered while providing nursing care in Canada. While the examination does not test candidates' knowledge of specific values, beliefs, and practices linked to individual cultures, it is intended to measure awareness, sensitivity, and respect for diverse cultural values, beliefs, and practices. Cultural issues are integrated within the examination without introducing cultural stereotypes.

Client Health Situation

In the development of the RN Exam, the client is viewed holistically. Thus, the client's biophysical, psychosocial, and spiritual dimensions form the basis of every health situation. The particular client health situations to be depicted on the examination are based on the assumptions on which the competencies are founded.

On the basis of the specified contextual variables and the elements mentioned above (i.e., the holistic dimensions of the client, stable and unstable health situations across the client's life cycle), different examination questions are developed that test a cross-section of client health situations.

Health Care Environment

One of the assumptions underlying the competencies is that "The practice environment of the entry-level registered nurse can be any setting or circumstance within which nursing is practised. It includes, but is not limited to, the site of activity (e.g., institutions, clinics, homes, communities), programs designed to address client health, and resources available to the client and nurse." Furthermore, many competencies are applicable to a variety of settings.

For the purposes of the RN Exam, the health care environment is specified only where it is required to provide guidance to the candidate.

Summary Chart: RN Exam Development Guidelines

COMPETENCIES	
Group 1: 45 to 50% of questions	**Group 2: 50 to 55% of questions**

STRUCTURAL VARIABLES	
Examination Length and Format	240-260 objective questions (i.e., multiple choice)
Test Equating	English and French anchor questions are used to accomplish test equating
Question Presentation	45 to 55% independent questions 45 to 55% case-based questions
Taxonomies for Questions: Cognitive Domain Affective Domain	Knowledge/Comprehension: 25-30% of questions Application: 40-50% of questions Critical Thinking: 20-30% of questions Receiving/Responding Valuing } 4-8% of questions Organization/Characterization
Competency Categories and Weightings	Nurse Client Relationship: 9% Health Promotion: 16% Illness/Injury Prevention: 11% Curative/Supportive Care: 40% Rehabilitative Care: 9% Professional Practice: 16%

CONTEXTUAL VARIABLES	
Client Type	Individual Client 50-60% Family 15-25% Group Population } 15-25%* Community
Client Age and Gender	**Male** **Female** 0 to 18 years 12-18% 12-18% 19 to 64 years 14-20% 15-21% 65 to 79 years 5-10% 15-20% 80+ years 1-3% 5-10%
Client Culture	Questions will be included that measure awareness, sensitivity, and respect for different cultural values, beliefs, and practices, without introducing stereotypes.
Client Health Situation	The client is viewed holistically within the context of stable and unstable health situations across the client's life cycle. The client's health situations will be based on the assumptions on which the competencies are founded.
Health Care Environment	The practice environment of the entry-level registered nurse can be any setting or circumstance within which nursing is practised. Most of the competencies are not setting dependent. The health care environment will be specified where necessary.

* For the 2000 and 2001 versions of the RN Exam, the proportion of questions within this category will be set at the lower limit of the specified range (i.e., 15%).

How the RN Exam is Organized

The RN Exam is divided into two books, administered over the course of one day; Book I is written in the morning, and Book II in the afternoon. You will have 3 1/2 hours to write each book. The exam consists of a series of multiple-choice questions, each of which is designed to measure a specific competency expected of nurses beginning to practise.

Each question on the exam, whether in the case or independent format, contains a stem and four options. The stem is typically made up of one to three sentences that provide relevant information or data, and the specific nursing question that is being asked. Of the four options, one is the correct (or best) answer, and the remaining three are incorrect, or less correct options.

Some of the questions in each exam book are *experimental*. That is, they are being tried out to determine their suitability for use on future exams. Although your answers to these experimental questions do not count toward your score, it is important to do your best on each question on the exam because you have no way of knowing which questions are experimental.

The sample case and independent questions below show the types of questions used in the exam. Note that the questions in these examples are not meant to reflect the level of difficulty of the questions on the exam. Correct answers are blackened in the ovals on the right.

2

SAMPLE QUESTIONS: CASE-BASED

Case 1

Mr. Robert Lowry, an 82-year-old married man, collapses at home. Mr. Lowry is rushed to the community hospital where it is determined that he has suffered a cerebrovascular accident (CVA). Mrs. Lowry tells the nurse that, prior to this incident, her husband had been taking a thiazine diuretic to control his hypertension.

QUESTIONS 1 to 5 refer to this case.

1. Which one of the following initial nursing assessments would determine Mr. Lowry's level of consciousness?

    1. Visual fields
    2. Auditory acuity
    3. Deep tendon reflexes
    4. Responses to painful stimuli　　　　　　　　　　　①②③●

2. Mr. Lowry regains consciousness and is found to have loss of movement on his left side and hemianopsia. Which one of the following responses by the nurse would be appropriate to give Mrs. Lowry when she asks questions regarding her husband's potential for recovery?

    1. "It's difficult to know, but most people take at least a year to recover completely."
    2. "It sounds as though you may be somewhat anxious to resume your former lifestyle."
    3. "Concern about recovery is common. Rehabilitation takes time and progress is often slow."
    4. "To be anxious is normal. Unfortunately, there is no way of estimating your husband's recovery potential."　　　　①②●④

3. Mr. Lowry is receiving a thiazide diuretic. Which one of the following manifestations would indicate mild hypokalemia?

    1. Anorexia
    2. Bradycardia
    3. Muscle spasms
    4. Elevated blood pressure　　　　　　　　●②③④

4. Which one of the following interventions should the nurse implement to encourage Mr. Lowry to feed himself?

1. Assist him to position the cutlery in his hands.
2. Suggest that Mrs. Lowry take him to the cafeteria.
3. Arrange food items on his tray so he can see them.
4. Allow sufficient time for him to cut up his own food. ①②●④

5. Which one of the following nursing observations of Mrs. Lowry's behaviour would best indicate her readiness to participate in her husband's care at home?

1. She visits him every day.
2. She selects his daily menus.
3. She brings his shaving kit and pyjamas from home.
4. She asks if she is correctly positioned to help him walk. ①②③●

SAMPLE QUESTIONS: INDEPENDENT

1. Which one of the following nursing measures would most likely facilitate a client's acceptance of an altered body image following a total laryngectomy and tracheostomy?

1. Demonstrate a sympathetic approach when providing the client's tracheostomy care.
2. Emphasize what the client can do within the limitations resulting from the treatment.
3. Encourage the client's family to refrain from discussing the tracheostomy while visiting.
4. Reassure the client that following discharge there can be a complete return to prehospitalization activities. ①●③④

2. What should the nurse do if, in the nurse's opinion, the physician's order for a postoperative analgesic seems excessive?

1. Assess the client closely for side effects after giving the medication.
2. Seek clarification from the physician before giving the medication.
3. Give the medication and document the concern in the nursing notes.
4. Withhold the medication and document the reason in the nursing notes. ①●③④

Chapter 3
Test-taking strategies

Test-Taking Strategies

This chapter will help you prepare to write the RN Exam by reviewing what you need to do before and during the exam, what to bring to the examination centre, and how you can best perform on multiple-choice questions.

Before the RN Exam
❗ Arrange to Write the RN Exam

To write the RN Exam, you must arrange to do so by contacting the RN regulatory authority in the province or territory in which you wish to write. Their staff will inform you of the documentation you must provide to register for the exam, as well as the fee you will have to pay. A list of RN regulatory authorities that use the RN Exam, can be found in Appendix B.

All candidates are entitled to receive a fair and valid assessment. To this end, the Canadian Nurses Association and Assessment Strategies Inc., in conjunction with the regulatory authorities, will authorize reasonable and appropriate modifications to the RN Exam administration procedures, to accommodate candidates with disabilities. For further information, contact the regulatory authority in your jurisdiction.

❗ Read *The Canadian RN Exam Prep Guide*

This guide, including the CD-ROM, contains information that will help you become more familiar with the RN Exam. The rationales for the correct answers (and the incorrect options), and the references listed in the Bibliography, provide an ideal way to review essential nursing content. You are also presented with a variety of ways to use the *Prep Guide* and CD-ROM, depending on how much time you have before you write the RN Exam.

❗ Take the Practice Exam in the *Prep Guide*

Taking the Practice Exam under conditions that are as close as possible to those of the actual exam is a great way to prepare and to ensure that there will be no surprises. Give yourself the right amount of time to complete each exam book and don't look ahead to the answers. To simulate true exam conditions, arrange to take the Practice Exam with other students who are also interested in preparing for the exam.

❗ Use the Information from Your Performance Profile

By conducting an analysis of your performance on the Practice Exam, you will be able to identify your strengths and weaknesses. Use this information to your advantage to focus your studying in areas of weakness. If you are taking the paper and pencil version of the exam, use the information on how to create your Performance Profile found in Chapter 6. With the CD-ROM version, your Performance Profile is generated automatically.

❗ Study Effectively

Select a place that is quiet and free from distractions, yet comfortable for studying. Develop a study plan schedule, dividing your time between specific topics or sections. Keep in mind that five 2-hour sessions are likely to be more beneficial than two 5-hour periods. Monitor your progress and revise your schedule as necessary.

❗ Prepare for the Examination Day

Check the location of the examination centre and examination room, and determine how much time you will need to get there. If necessary, do a practice run and confirm bus schedules or the availability of parking. As well, it is important to be alert and focused when you write the exam—be sure to get plenty of rest, and to eat a suitable breakfast, before you arrive at the examination centre.

3

The Canadian RN Exam Prep Guide

What to Bring to the RN Exam

❗ Identification

In most cases, you must bring your candidate identification card, issued by your RN regulatory authority. They will also inform you whether you are required to present additional identification.

❗ Pencils/Eraser

Unless otherwise advised, take two or three medium-soft (HB) pencils and a soft pencil eraser.

❗ A Watch

Although each examination room will have a clock, and you will be periodically advised of the time, you might prefer to bring your own watch to keep track of the time and gauge your pace.

What NOT to Bring

Books, paper, notes, calculators, and other aids are *not* permitted in the examination room.

What to Wear

Remember that you will be sitting for hours. Wear comfortable clothing.

During the RN Exam

❗ Listen to All Announcements

The presiding officer will inform you of important details, such as how long you have to complete the exam and how and where to hand in your exam book and answer sheet, as well as when you should arrive for the second session.

❗ Read the Exam Book Instructions

Exam instructions are very important. It is essential that you have a clear understanding of what you are expected to do. If you don't understand what you have been told or what you have read, ask questions in the period before the exam officially begins.

❗ Complete All Information Accurately

You will be required to fill in certain information on your answer sheets and exam books (e.g., your candidate number from your identification card). Errors made in completing this information can delay the scoring of your exam. And if you make errors in recording your choice of answer, you will not be given any credit. Be sure that for each question you have recorded a single answer in the appropriate place on the answer sheet.

❗ One Question at a Time

Consider each question as a separate entity. Don't let a difficult question make you anxious as you approach the next one. Do the best you can with each question and move on to the next. Try not to rush, but don't spend more than two or three minutes on any individual question. If you don't know the answer, skip it and return to it later. Something in a subsequent case or question might jog your memory. If you still don't know the answer, don't be afraid to guess. No points are deducted for wrong answers. If you do not answer all the questions in sequence, it is particularly important to ensure that the oval you are filling in on your answer sheet is aligned with the correct question number.

When you decide on a correct answer from among the options, immediately indicate your choice on the answer sheet before moving on to the next question. Do not circle all the answers in the exam book and transfer them when you have finished the book because you could run out of time, and credit is not given for answers in your exam book—only for answers recorded on your answer sheet.

❗ Changing Your Answer

If you decide to change an answer after filling it in on your answer sheet, make sure the original choice is completely erased. Otherwise, it will appear as though you have selected two options. This will be scored as a wrong answer. Similarly, avoid making stray marks on your answer sheet that the computer could inadvertently pick up as answers to questions.

Be cautious about changing your answer. Very often your first choice is correct. Making a new selection is only advantageous if you are confident that the new option is correct.

❗ Read the Question Carefully
Concentrate on what is being asked in the question and relate it to the data provided. Do not make any assumptions unless they are directly implied.

Pick out important words that relate to the question. For example, in some questions you may be asked for the most appropriate *initial* response by the nurse; but you should be aware that questions that follow may deal with the nurse's most *ethical* response or the nurse's most *therapeutic* response. Reviewing the questions in the Practice Exam will help you to recognize key words that will appear on the RN Exam.

❗ Guessing
There is no penalty for guessing on the RN Exam. You will not lose any marks if you select an incorrect answer.

Strategies for Multiple-Choice Questions
❗ Familiarize Yourself with Multiple-Choice Questions
A thorough understanding of multiple-choice questions will allow you to most effectively apply your nursing knowledge and skills to the testing situation.

A multiple-choice question is constructed so that only someone who has mastered the subject matter will select the correct answer; to that person, only one option appears to be the correct answer. To someone who lacks a firm grasp of the subject matter, all options look equally attractive and plausible.

❗ Use a Three-Step Approach
It is often helpful to use the following three-step approach to answer the multiple-choice questions that appear on the RN Exam.

1. Carefully read the information provided in the case text (for cases) and in the stem of the question. Try to understand the client's health situation and the nursing care the client is likely to require.

2. Read the stem carefully. Before looking at the options, make sure you have understood the question. Use the information provided and, based on your nursing knowledge and skills, try to imagine the correct answer.

3. Study the alternatives provided and select the one that comes closest to the answer you imagined. You may wish to reread the stem before finalizing your selection.

❗ Take Advantage of the Process of Elimination
If you are not presented with an option that matches or is close to the one you imagined after reading the stem, try to eliminate some of the options that are absolutely incorrect.

The Canadian RN
Exam Prep Guide

The following example illustrates how you can benefit from the process of elimination.

Question

Which one of the following responses by the nurse would best assist Mrs. Clement to verbalize her fears when she expresses anxiety about the possibility of having a mastectomy?
1. "I know exactly how you feel about this."
2. "Would you like to talk to the head nurse?"
3. "You seem worried that you may need to have surgery."
4. "It's a normal reaction to be afraid when faced with surgery."

To take full advantage of the process of elimination, it is important to focus on the key idea in the stem. The key idea is assisting the client to verbalize her fears. In Option 1, the focus is on the nurse and not on the client or her concerns. Option 1 can be eliminated because it is highly unlikely that any one person knows exactly how someone else feels in a given situation.

Option 2 also fails to address the client's immediate concern because the nurse completely avoids dealing with the client and passes the responsibility on to another team member. For this reason, Option 2 can be eliminated as a possible correct answer.

Option 4 should be eliminated immediately. By telling the client that what she is experiencing is "normal," the nurse implies that the client's situation is routine. Such a response would be depersonalizing and nontherapeutic.

After these three options are systematically eliminated, you can consider Option 3, the correct option, which is open-ended and encourages the client to begin talking about how she feels about her upcoming surgery.

Checklist of Common Test-Taking Errors

Students often make mistakes on an examination because of errors in processing facts and information, or because of problems with multiple-choice questions. These are technical errors related to writing tests and not related to a lack of nursing knowledge or skill.

As you proceed through the Practice Exam and determine whether you answered questions correctly, you may wish to keep a checklist of problems you had related to your test-taking skills. You can then use the results of this checklist to identify skills that you need to develop during your preparation for the RN Exam.

A Checklist of Common Test-Taking Errors is provided on page 23. Some of the most common errors are listed down the left-hand column. Tick off the particular technical error(s) you made with the questions you answered incorrectly. Keep in mind that you may have more than one technical error with any one question.

CHECKLIST OF COMMON TEST-TAKING ERRORS	
Missed important information in the case test	
Misread the stem of the question	
Failed to pick out important or key words in the stem of the question	
Did not relate the question to information in the case text	
Made assumptions in the case text/question	
Focused on insignificant details and missed key issues	
Selected more than one answer	
Incorrectly transferred answer from selection in exam book to computer answer sheet	
Switched answer selected	
Other:	

3

Chapter 4
Taking the practice exam

Taking the Practice Exam

Like the RN Exam, the Practice Exam consists of two books: Book I and Book II. How you completed the Practice Exam will depend on whether you are using Method A, B, or C (described in Chapter 1). If you are going to take the Practice Exam only once, gain the maximum benefit from this experience by attempting to simulate the actual exam conditions as closely as possible. That means writing the exam in a quiet location, without the benefit of books, notes or other aids, and strictly adhering to the time limit.

Since there are no experimental questions being tested on the Practice Exam (i.e., all the questions will count toward your total score), you should limit yourself to 3 hours per exam book. During the RN Exam, you will have experimental questions in the exam books; therefore, you will be allowed 3 1/2 hours per book.

Read the instructions contained in the Practice Exam carefully, but keep in mind that during your simulation, you will not have the benefit of a presiding officer to remind you of how much time is remaining. The front cover of the Practice Exam and the instructions are similar to those on the RN Exam. The instructions indicate that you have 3 1/2 hours (administration time limit for the actual RN Exam) but, as suggested above, you should limit yourself to 3 hours per book during your simulation. On the cover of each Practice Exam book is a *test form number* that is also repeated in the lower left-hand corner of each page of the exam book. This test form number is required by Assessment Strategies Inc. for scoring the RN Exam but not the Practice Exam as you will be scoring your own Practice Exam.

There are blank answer sheets included with the *Prep Guide* so that you can gain experience in recoding the personal information and filling in the ovals that correspond to your answer selections. Familiarize yourself with the candidate information you will be required to complete when you write the RN Exam.

You should wait until you have finished the entire Practice Exam to calculate your total score and to create your Performance Profile. The information will be complete and, therefore, more accurate and more useful to you. Instructions on calculating your score and determining your Performance Profile are provided in Chapters 5 and 6, which follow the Practice Exam.

If you prefer taking the Practice Exam on the computer using the enclosed CD-ROM, your result and Performance Profile will be generated automatically once you have completed the exam in the testing mode.

4

Canadian Registered Nurse Examination

CANDIDATE NUMBER

_____

SIGNATURE

Book 1

Test Form 01910

READ THE INSTRUCTIONS AND SAMPLE QUESTIONS INSIDE THE FRONT COVER

CANADIAN NURSES ASSOCIATION
ASSOCIATION DES INFIRMIÈRES ET INFIRMIERS DU CANADA

INSTRUCTIONS

A) TESTING TIME AND MATERIAL

You will have three and one-half hours to work on this test. The starting and finishing times will be announced and you will be advised when there are 30 and 15 minutes working time remaining. If at any time you have any questions about what you should do, raise your hand and an invigilator will assist you.

You will be advised whether you may leave the examination room if you finish the test before the time is up. You must stop working when the signal is given. An invigilator will check your test book and answer sheet before you leave.

Clear your desk of all materials except your identification card, answer sheet, test book, pencils, and eraser. Do not fold, bend, or tear your answer sheet, as this could affect the scoring of your test.

B) ANSWER SHEET

Complete the identification portion of your answer sheet. Print your name, date of birth and date of the examination. Print and fill in the test form number (from the cover of your test book).

If you have a candidate label provided with your identification card: detach the label from the identification card and place the label in the appropriate location on the answer sheet. Do **not** fill in the information to the right of the candidate label unless the candidate label is incorrect. **If you do not have a candidate label:** fill the oval corresponding to the language of writing, print your candidate number and writing centre code, and fill the corresponding oval for each digit.

Be sure the mark you make for each answer is black, fills the oval, and contains the number corresponding to the number of the answer you have chosen. Do **not** fill in more than one oval for a question or you will get no credit for it. Erase **completely** any answer you wish to change and mark your new choice in the correct oval. An incomplete erasure may be read incorrectly as an intended answer. Do not press too heavily on your pencil or you may damage the answer sheet.

Note that the questions on the answer sheet are numbered in columns. There are fewer questions in the test book than there are numbers on the answer sheet.

Make no stray marks on the answer sheet; they may count against you. You may use the margins of the test book for any scratch work, but you will *not* get credit for anything you write in the test book.

C) TEST BOOK

Sign your name on the line on the cover of this book and copy your candidate number into the appropriate boxes. If you do not have a candidate number, **print** your name under your signature.

Read each question carefully and choose the answer that you think is the **best** of the four alternatives presented. If you cannot decide on an answer to a question, go on to the next one and come back to this question later if you have time. Try to answer all questions. Marks are not subtracted for wrong answers. If you are not sure of an answer, it will be to your advantage to guess. It will probably be best to start at the beginning of the test and work through the questions in order.

This examination contains a number of experimental questions being tested for future use. Your answers to these questions will **not** count toward your score. Because you will not be able to tell which questions are experimental, you should do your best on all questions, but do *not* spend too much time on any question.

The questions in the examination may be presented in nursing cases or as independent questions. The context of some cases may seem similar to others in your test book. This reflects current practice where a nurse may have to care for different clients with similar problems. Each case, however, tests different nursing content. The sample case on the next page shows the types of questions used. Correct answers are blackened in the ovals on the right.

Sample Case

Sally Bowman, 15 years old, is 3 months pregnant. She has been referred to the community health nurse for prenatal counseling and teaching. During the interview with the nurse, Sally states that she smokes about 20-25 cigarettes per day.

QUESTIONS 1 to 5 refer to this case.

1. Sally tells the nurse that it was not her idea to visit the nurse and that she is unsure about returning. Which one of the following responses by the nurse best demonstrates a helping attitude?

   1. "Would you like me to arrange for you to see another nurse?"
   2. "Some of your friends must be very worried about you."
   3. "I wonder what ideas you have for how we can work together?"
   4. "If getting here is difficult, I can arrange to see you wherever it is convenient for you."

   ① ② ● ④

2. At the end of their interview, Sally tells the nurse that she thinks she will continue to smoke. Which one of the following adolescent developmental tasks should the nurse identify as the most likely barrier to smoking cessation?

   1. Accepting a changing body image
   2. Establishing a value system
   3. Striving for independence and maturity
   4. Seeking social stability

   ① ② ● ④

3. Which one of the following statements by the nurse best reflects the appropriate application of the principles of communication?

   1. "Are you aware of how harmful smoking is to both you and your baby?"
   2. "Let's talk about getting you enrolled in our Stop Smoking Program."
   3. "Can you tell me how long you have been smoking and why you started?"
   4. "Tell me how you feel about the effect of smoking on your baby."

   ① ② ③ ●

4. At Sally's next visit 1 month later, she tells the nurse that she has been able to decrease the number of cigarettes she smokes to 5 -10 per day. Which one of the following long-term goals is Sally most likely working toward?

   1. A decrease in the incidence of neonatal respiratory disorders
   2. A decrease in the risk of fetal growth retardation
   3. An increase in potential fetal iron stores
   4. A decrease in the incidence of fetal congenital anomalies

   ● ② ③ ④

5. Pat is a colleague who is observing the nurse's developing relationship with Sally. Pat remarks to the nurse, "You seem to be spending a great deal of time with Sally. Are you sure this isn't affecting your other clients?" Which of the following actions should the nurse take first in response to Pat's comments?

   1. Present Pat's concerns to another colleague for validation.
   2. Re-evaluate the relationship with Sally and the possible need for change.
   3. Clarify Pat's comments and ask her to elaborate on her concern.
   4. Verify with the other clients their level of satisfaction with the care provided.

   ① ② ● ④

End of sample case

DO NOT OPEN YOUR TEST BOOK OR BEGIN WORKING
UNTIL THE SIGNAL IS GIVEN TO DO SO

Case 1

Mrs. Richards, 35 years old, is at the 29th week of her 4th pregnancy. Her previous obstetrical history includes 2 spontaneous abortions. Her last pregnancy ended at 30 weeks gestation due to severe pre-eclampsia. The child, Thomas, is now 3 years old and has some minor growth and developmental difficulties. In the current pregnancy, Mrs. Richards is showing signs and symptoms of recurring pre-eclampsia and is admitted to the antepartum unit for monitoring. Mrs. Richards and her husband are worried about child care for Thomas. Although Mrs. Richards acknowledges the necessity of hospital admission and possibility of pre-term delivery, she wants to return home as soon as possible.

QUESTIONS 1 to 6 refer to this case.

1. Which of the following interventions takes priority in addressing Mr. and Mrs. Richards' needs at this time?

    1. Organize a visit to the neonatal intensive care nursery for them to meet the staff and see the environment.
    2. Explain to them that complete bed rest will help to decrease blood pressure and promote diuresis.
    3. Ask Mr. Richards if he could take a leave of absence to care for Thomas.
    4. Refer them to the social worker to assist them in obtaining immediate child care for Thomas.

2. After 3 days of hospitalization, Mrs. Richards' blood pressure ranges from 130/80 to 150/100 mmHg. The physician questions the accuracy of the blood pressure readings. Which of the following factors is important to consider when assessing blood pressure?

    1. Blood pressure should be measured on the same arm with the client in the same position each time.
    2. Manual and electronic blood pressure assessment devices will provide the same readings.
    3. A sitting blood pressure more accurately reflects a pregnancy hypertensive state than a lying blood pressure.
    4. Blood pressure should be assessed at the same time each day without consideration of prior events.

3. Mrs. Richards' pre-eclampsia stabilizes and she is discharged. During the drive home, Mr. and Mrs. Richards are involved in an automobile accident. Mrs. Richards has been subjected to an abdominal impact injury and is brought directly to the Labour and Delivery Unit. Which of the following nursing interventions takes priority in this situation?

    1. Begin a 24-hour urine collection for assessment of estriol levels.
    2. Assess for the presence of abdominal pain and vaginal bleeding.
    3. Perform a vaginal examination to assess cervical changes.
    4. Apply an internal fetal monitor to assess fetal heart rate.

4. Mrs. Richards has been diagnosed with a grade 1 degree of abruptio placentae. There is minimal separation with some vaginal bleeding, but no evidence of fetal distress. Which of the following actual or potential problems should be identified in the nursing plan of care for this particular situation?

    1. Fluid volume deficit related to loss of fluid into interstitial space
    2. Altered respiratory function and ineffective breathing patterns related to pain
    3. Risk for alteration in cardiac output related to increased circulatory volume
    4. Risk for fetal injury related to decreased uterine/placental perfusion

5. Twenty-four hours later, Mrs. Richards' blood pressure increases to 160/110 mmHg and she has increased vaginal bleeding. The obstetrical resident on call does not wish to inform the client's attending physician and decides to continue to observe her condition. The Richards are very upset and request that "something be done." Which of the following would demonstrate advocacy for the client by the nurse?

    1. Arrange for the Richards to meet the neonatology team to discuss the potential needs of the infant if it were delivered prematurely.
    2. Suggest that the Richards discuss their worries with the hospital social worker or client advocate.
    3. Discuss the Richards' concerns with the resident, and call the attending physician if he still will not place the call.
    4. Advise Mr. Richards to phone the attending physician himself in order to get immediate action.

[handwritten: nurse is the one who talk to dr. regarding pt's concern]

6. Mrs. Richards undergoes an emergency caesarean section to deliver the fetus. Despite all efforts at resuscitation, the infant dies. Which of the following nursing interventions would demonstrate sensitivity to the Richards' needs?

    1. Ask the Richards if they would like to have the baby brought into the room.
    2. Arrange to have a photograph of the infant taken and give it to the Richards.
    3. Reassure the Richards that this event will not prevent future pregnancies.
    4. Place a "No visitors" sign on the Richards' door.

End of case 1

Case 2

Mrs. Kite is brought to the hospital by two co-workers. Her co-workers inform the nurse that Mrs. Kite has been experiencing lightheadedness, double vision, and slurred speech, over the last hour. Mrs. Kite was diagnosed with diabetes mellitus 12 months ago.

QUESTIONS 7 to 12 refer to this case.

7. While doing Mrs. Kite's admission history, which of the following responses by Mrs. Kite would lead the nurse to believe that she has managed hypoglycemia effectively in the past?

    1. "When I feel like this I usually eat a large candy bar."
    2. "When I feel like this I usually eat a peanut butter sandwich."
    3. "When I feel like this I usually have a glass of orange juice."
    4. "When I feel like this I usually have a few cookies with ice-cream."

8. Mrs. Kite is treated for her hypoglycemia; however, her condition worsens. She demonstrates disoriented behaviour, slurred speech and much difficulty arousing. Her blood glucose level continues to fall. Which of the following actions should the nurse anticipate?

    1. Offer her a protein and starch snack.
    2. Administer 1 mg of glucagon hydrochloride (Glucagon) IM.
    3. Start an intravenous of 5% dextrose in water (D5W).
    4. Obtain STAT serum glucose.

9. Mrs. Kite's condition stabilizes and the physician orders metformin hydrochloride (Glucophage) 500 mg, q 6h, p.o., on discharge. What amount of medication should the client take in 24 hours?

    1. 1 g
    2. 1.5 g
    3. 2 g
    4. 3 g

10. Mrs. Kite's physician orders 12 units of regular insulin and 20 units of NPH insulin before breakfast. Which of the following demonstrations by the client would indicate to the nurse that she understands the correct procedure for insulin administration?

    1. With an insulin syringe, she injects 20 units of air into the NPH vial. With the same syringe, she injects 12 units of air into the regular insulin and removes the same amount of insulin. She then returns to the NPH and withdraws 20 units.
    2. Before mixing different types of insulin, she rotates each vial of insulin and vigorously shakes them until bubbles form.
    3. With an insulin syringe, she injects 12 units of air into the regular insulin. With the same syringe, she injects 20 units of air into the NPH vial and removes the same amount of insulin. She then returns to the regular insulin and withdraws 12 units.
    4. She pinches up the skin and enters on a 45 degree angle, aspirates, injects the mixture and withdraws the syringe. She concludes by vigorously massaging the site.

11. Mrs. Kite tells the nurse that she enjoys jogging with her friends. She admits that she sometimes feels unwell after jogging and goes to bed hoping the feeling will pass. What should the nurse recommend?

    1. The client should stop jogging and take up an alternate form of activity that is less strenuous.
    2. The client should eat a carbohydrate and protein snack before jogging.
    3. The client should test her blood sugar before her jog, and if it is too high, she should not go jogging.
    4. The client should eat a chocolate bar if she feels weak and resume jogging with her friends.

12. Mrs. Kite is eager to understand more about her diabetes. She admits that she pays little attention to what she eats and drinks. When helping Mrs. Kite make appropriate meal choices, what should the nurse reinforce with the client?

    1. Meal planning should include a balanced food selection and control of caloric intake.
    2. Meals should be planned to increase caloric intake from fat.
    3. She can successfully manage her diet by only using Canada's Food Guide.
    4. There should be an equal intake of carbohydrates and fats.

End of case 2

Case 3

Mr. Harris, a 30-year-old single lawyer, is brought to the emergency department in an ambulance. He is accompanied by his roommate, who states that when he got home at 22 00, he found Mr. Harris slumped in a chair and unresponsive to his efforts to rouse him.

QUESTIONS 13 to 18 refer to this case.

13. When collecting data for Mr. Harris' admission history, which of the following questions should the nurse ask Mr. Harris' roommate to obtain the most significant information?

    1. "How long have you and Mr. Harris been roommates?"
    2. "What can you tell me about Mr. Harris that would help us determine what has happened?"
    3. "Have you contacted Mr. Harris' family to ask them to come to the hospital as soon as possible?"
    4. "Have you ever found Mr. Harris unconscious before?"

14. Mr. Harris' roommate tells the nurse that the client is a "party animal" and for the past 6 months he has been not only drinking a lot of alcohol but also using cocaine. Recently, Mr. Harris' performance at work has deteriorated. A blood test for alcohol and drug screen indicates high levels of alcohol and cocaine, as well as traces of lorazepam (Ativan). Which of the following complications in Mr. Harris' condition should the nurse anticipate?

    1. Respiratory arrest and cardiac arrhythmias
    2. Seizures and flashbacks
    3. Toxic psychosis and coronary artery vasodilatation
    4. Delirium tremens and hyperthermia

15. Which of the following interventions should be given priority in caring for Mr. Harris?

    1. Position in low Fowler's, maintain a quiet and safe environment, assess for injuries requiring immediate medical attention.
    2. Take blood glucose readings q 2h, apply a condom catheter to monitor urine output, keep client warm.
    3. Notify parents, monitor respirations and level of consciousness q 1h, prepare for nasogastric tube insertion.
    4. Maintain a patent airway, perform a neurological assessment q 15min, and initiate parenteral fluid therapy.

16. Mr. Harris recovers consciousness and is transferred to the in-patient psychiatric unit. Which of the following goals should be a priority in Mr. Harris' discharge plan from the hospital?

    1. He takes responsibility for his own behaviour.
    2. He considers joining a support group.
    3. He explains his difficulties with the pressures of being a young lawyer.
    4. He gains insight into the reasons for his substance abuse.

17. Which of the following community resources should the nurse assist Mr. Harris in contacting after his discharge from the hospital?

    1. Community health nurse
    2. Substance abuse support group
    3. Alanon
    4. Methadone clinic

18. Mr. Harris' primary nurse overhears one of the other nurses on the team inviting Mr. Harris to a party at her apartment after he is discharged. What is the most appropriate action by the primary nurse?

    1. Not interfere.
    2. Report her colleague to the professional association.
    3. Tell the client he shouldn't attend.
    4. Speak with the colleague about her behaviour.

End of case 3

Case 4

Mr. Jacobs, 53 years old, 90 kg, is home watching the final game of the National Hockey League series after a dinner of pizza and beer. His wife becomes very concerned when she notices that he is pale, has beads of sweat on his forehead and is rubbing his left arm repeatedly. Although Mr. Jacobs keeps saying that he is fine, his wife calls the ambulance to have him brought in to the local community hospital.

QUESTIONS 19 to 24 refer to this case.

19. When assessing Mr. Jacobs in the emergency department, which of the following sources of information will best assist the nurse to plan the care for the client?

    1. Mr. Jacobs
    2. Mrs. Jacobs
    3. Past health records
    4. Ambulance attendant

20. Mr. Jacobs is feeling a little short of breath and complains of chest pain. The nurse initiates oxygen by nasal canulla. Mrs. Jacobs looks perplexed and asks the nurse how oxygen is going to help her husband's chest pain. Which response by the nurse will help Mr. and Mrs. Jacobs understand the care provided?

    1. "The doctor has ordered oxygen to help with the shortness of breath."
    2. "Your husband's heart muscle may be working hard and supplying it with additional oxygen may help decrease the pain."
    3. "Oxygen is a routine standard of care for anyone complaining of chest pain. It will ease the symptoms quickly."
    4. "I will let the physician know that you have questions regarding your husband's condition."

21. Mr. Jacobs is transferred in stable condition to the stepdown coronary care unit with a diagnosis of unstable angina. His orders include: bedrest, oxygen p.r.n., a saline lock, metoprolol (Lopressor) b.i.d., sublingual nitroglycerin (Nitrostat) p.r.n., sublingual lorazepam (Ativan) p.r.n. After going to the bathroom, he complains of substernal chest pain and restlessness. What should be the nurse's priority interventions?

    1. Obtain vital signs, apply oxygen, administer an additional dose of metoprolol, call physician.
    2. Obtain vital signs, apply oxygen, administer Ativan, monitor for increased level of pain.
    3. Assess pain, apply oxygen, administer nitroglycerin q 5min until the pain subsides.
    4. Apply oxygen, obtain vital signs, administer nitroglycerin x 3 p.r.n., inform physician.

22. Mr. Jacobs' condition deteriorates and he develops crackles in his lower lobes of the lungs and is feeling short of breath and anxious. The physician orders morphine sulphate (Morphine) 4 mg IV and furosemide (Lasix) 40 mg IV. Which of the following changes in condition best indicates that Mr. Jacobs is responding favourably to the medications?

    1. Decreased respiratory rate, decreased crackles
    2. Decreased crackles, large diuresis
    3. Increased pulse, increased respiratory rate
    4. Decreased respiratory rate, decreased blood pressure

23. Mr. Jacobs' condition is stable and he is being monitored on telemetry. He has been sleeping at infrequent periods and is restless and irritable. Mrs. Jacobs remains at his bedside constantly. The nurse enters the room to take Mr. Jacobs' vital signs and finds him sleeping. What should be the nurse's intervention?

    1. Take Mr. Jacobs' vital signs.
    2. Ask Mrs. Jacobs to call the nurse when her husband awakens.
    3. Delay the assessment and adjust the plan of care to allow for 90-minute periods of uninterrupted sleep.
    4. Gently awaken him, take his vital signs quickly, encourage him to return to sleep, and offer him a sedative.

24. Mr. Jacobs and his wife are attending the hospital's cardiac teaching class on low cholesterol diets. When they return to the room the nurse asks them if they have any questions or comments. Mrs. Jacobs states that she is anxious to start cooking differently, while Mr. Jacobs states that he cannot just eat "rabbit food." What should be the nurse's response?

    1. "You have been eating a diet that is low in cholesterol while in the hospital and have been eating everything on your tray."
    2. "You will only have to follow this diet until your cholesterol is under control."
    3. "The risk for heart disease doubles when the blood cholesterol is elevated. A low cholesterol diet may not mean giving up the foods you like."
    4. "Your wife appears to understand the relationship between heart disease and blood cholesterol, and I am sure she will help you meet your nutritional needs."

End of case 4

Case 5

Mr. Hyman, a 60-year-old accountant, is transferred by stretcher to the hospital, unconscious, with left-sided weakness, and in a supine position. The nurse observes that Mr. Hyman's respirations are laboured and stridorous, and he is cyanotic. Secretions are drooling from the left side of his mouth.

QUESTIONS 25 to 30 refer to this case.

25. What immediate action(s) should the nurse take?

    1. Place the client in a lateral or semi-prone position.
    2. Insert an oral airway.
    3. Leave the client on his back and begin suctioning immediately.
    4. Give the client mouth care and then position him on his left side.

26. The doctor orders IV therapy, 2/3 dextrose and 1/3 saline, at 75 ml per hour. At 08 00, 600 ml of solution remain to be absorbed. At what time should the nurse plan to hang the next bag?

    1. 14 30
    2. 16 00
    3. 18 30
    4. 20 00

27. Mr. Hyman is now conscious. A CT scan indicates focal damage to the right side of his brain. Which of the following interventions should the nurse implement to encourage Mr. Hyman to feed himself?

    1. Order a soft food diet and place utensils on the right side of his tray.
    2. Order a soft food diet and place utensils on the left side of his tray.
    3. Ask Mrs. Hyman to come in at mealtimes.
    4. Have Mr. Hyman sit with other clients at mealtimes.

28. Mr. Hyman will be discharged in two days. Mrs. Hyman is very concerned about being able to help her husband with his daily activities when he gets home. Which of the following interventions should the nurse implement to address Mrs. Hyman's concerns?

    1. Assess the resources available to Mrs. Hyman.
    2. Suggest that Mrs. Hyman hire a helper.
    3. Refer Mrs. Hyman to community services.
    4. Tell her to request help from family members.

29. Two days before discharge, Mr. Hyman is diagnosed with glaucoma in his left eye. The doctor orders levobunolol hydrochloride (Betagan) 1 gtt (OS) b.i.d.. How should the nurse proceed to teach Mrs. Hyman to instill the eye drops?

    1. Demonstrate the procedure for Mrs. Hyman, then observe her instill the drops.
    2. Use a mannequin to demonstrate the procedure to Mrs. Hyman.
    3. Give Mrs. Hyman a client-teaching sheet illustrating the procedure.
    4. Give Mrs. Hyman verbal instructions on how to instill the drops.

30. As Mr. Hyman's condition improves, he inquires about the possibility of returning to work. How should the nurse respond to his inquiry?

   1. Discuss with Mr. Hyman the possibility of retirement.
   2. Encourage Mr. Hyman to contact his employer about returning to work.
   3. Identify Mr. Hyman's specific concerns and refer him to the social worker.
   4. Explore with Mr. Hyman and the occupational therapist his interest in returning to work.

End of case 5

Case 6

Ms. Darcy, 22 years old, is admitted to the Intensive Care Burn Unit two hours after having sustained deep, partial thickness burns to 25% of her body, including her face, right arm, and chest. Ms. Darcy is placed in an isolation room. She has oxygen running via nasal prongs at 3 litres per minute, an IV infusing in her left arm, and there are doctor's orders for dressings, analgesics via Patient Controlled Analgesia (PCA) pump, and medications.

QUESTIONS 31 to 35 refer to this case.

31. What should be the nurse's priority in caring for Ms. Darcy?

   1. Assess the client's respiratory status.
   2. Assess the client's blood pressure and circulatory status.
   3. Activate the current doctor's orders.
   4. Ensure the patency of the infusing intravenous.

32. The nurse is setting up for the client's dressing change and notes that she has an inadequate supply of silver sulfadiazine (Flamazine). What should the nurse do?

   1. Leave the room and obtain the medication.
   2. Proceed with the dressing change, using the medication sparingly.
   3. Use Ms. Darcy's call bell to ask another nurse to bring the medication.
   4. Call for the unit clerk to bring the medication into the room.

33. While removing Ms. Darcy's dressings, the nurse notes that they are adhering to the wound bed in several places. Removal causes the client discomfort. To minimize the client's discomfort, what should the nurse document in her plan of care?

   1. Remove dressings as quickly as possible.
   2. Allow the client to remove dressings by herself.
   3. Administer Morphine bolus via PCA pump 1 hour prior to dressing change.
   4. Soak dressings with normal saline for at least 10 minutes prior to removal.

34. What assessment should be the nurse's priority when changing Ms. Darcy's medication from Morphine via PCA pump to oral Morphine?

   1. Level of consciousness
   2. Vital signs
   3. Level of pain
   4. Oxygen saturation

35. Ms. Darcy's fiancé enters her room while the nurse is doing her arm exercises. Her fiancé says: "Oh, sorry. I will come back when you are done." What would be the nurse's best response?

   1. "That would be great. We should be done in about 15 minutes."
   2. "You can stay. There are some chairs in the hallway that you can bring in."
   3. "If you stay, we can show you how to help with the exercises."
   4. "Please stay, we can do the exercises later."

End of case 6

Case 7

Mrs. Martin, 55 years old, comes to the community health clinic complaining of headaches and ankle edema. The nurse notes that Mrs. Martin is overweight. On arrival, her BP is 150/110 mmHg. She is diagnosed with essential hypertension and is started on chlorothiazide (Diuril) 500 mg p.o. b.i.d.

QUESTIONS 36 to 39 refer to this case.

36. Which one of the following assessments, recorded by the nurse, would have the greatest influence on Mrs. Martin's condition?

   1. Drinks one cup of coffee per day.
   2. Drinks alcohol on special occasions.
   3. Smokes one package of cigarettes a day.
   4. Father died at age 65 with prostatic cancer.

37. Which one of the following findings would indicate to the nurse that Mrs. Martin is responding positively to her chlorothiazide (Diuril)?

   1. A potassium level of 6 mEq/L.
   2. Blood pressure of 150/110 mmHg.
   3. An increase of 1 kg/day in her weight.
   4. Negative fluid balance of 500 ml per day.

38. Nurse Green reports that Mrs. Martin is still unsure of what foods are low in sodium, even though Nurse Smith completed the teaching yesterday. Nurse Green suggests that giving Mrs. Martin some sample menus would help. Which one of the following responses by Nurse Smith demonstrates an openness to new ideas?

   1. "It sounds as if you think I am not qualified to care for Mrs. Martin."
   2. "In the past, I have found that giving sample menus confuses clients."
   3. "Mrs. Martin expressed concern over meals; maybe some sample menus will help."
   4. "I think that providing sample menus is more appropriately performed by a dietician."

39. Before giving Mrs. Martin her antihypertensive medication, Nurse Jones neglects to check Mrs. Martin's blood pressure. Nurse Black, realizing this omission, tells Nurse Jones, "You should always check the blood pressure before administering the antihypertensive." Which one of the following responses would be most appropriate for Nurse Jones to make?

    1. "It's only a blood pressure; I don't think any harm was done."
    2. "I already knew that; it was included in my orientation material."
    3. "I must remember that; does that apply to all antihypertensive medications?"
    4. "I didn't think the blood pressure had to be checked if it was within the normal range."

End of case 7

Case 8

Eric Miles is a 4-year-old boy who was diagnosed with cystic fibrosis during infancy. Since Eric has experienced frequent respiratory infections in the past, the home care nurse visits regularly to monitor his situation and provide teaching to the family.

QUESTIONS 40 to 45 refer to this case.

40. Because Eric dislikes his treatment sessions, his parents perform postural drainage and percussion only when he is in the prone position watching television. The nurse should emphasize that postural drainage and percussion will be optimized when Eric is in which of the following positions?

    1. Sitting upright to drain the superior segments.
    2. In a supine position to drain the posterior segments.
    3. In a variety of positions to allow for drainage of all segments.
    4. Positioned with his chest lower than his abdomen to drain the anterior segments.

41. Mrs. Miles indicates that both she and her husband are frustrated with Eric's lack of cooperation during his postural drainage and percussion sessions. She also comments that they need help with this aspect of Eric's care. Which one of the following nursing interventions is most appropriate to facilitate their learning?

    1. Discuss the proper techniques for performing postural drainage and percussion.
    2. Suggest that the respiratory therapist visit daily to perform the postural drainage and percussion.
    3. Recommend that the treatments be done less often until the child is older and more cooperative.
    4. Assess the parents' understanding of growth and development when formulating a teaching plan to address their needs.

42. Mr. and Mrs. Miles are worried that Eric's illness has had a detrimental effect on his development, particularly his speech. Which one of the following assessment tools would be most appropriate for the nurse to use to evaluate Eric's language development?

    1. Apgar Score
    2. Snellen Screening Test
    3. Intelligence Quotient (IQ) Test
    4. Denver Developmental Screening Test

43. Which one of the following practices by Eric's parents would suggest a need for additional teaching by the home care nurse?

    1. Decreasing pancreatic enzymes if Eric is constipated.
    2. Increasing pancreatic enzymes as Eric's food intake increases.
    3. Administering pancreatic enzymes in the morning and at bedtime.
    4. Increasing pancreatic enzymes if Eric's stools are large and bulky.

44. Mr. and Mrs. Miles appear to be coping well, but they state that there are times when they feel very alone when dealing with the chronic aspects of Eric's condition. Which one of the following responses by the nurse would be most appropriate?

    1. "You seem depressed; talking to a counselor may relieve some of your concerns."
    2. "You appear to be coping fairly well. Although things may seem difficult now, they will improve."
    3. "I'm surprised you still feel this way. Most people who have children with cystic fibrosis find it less stressful by the end of the first year."
    4. "Many families who have children with cystic fibrosis experience similar feelings. Would you like me to arrange for you to talk with one of those families?"

45. The home care agency requests that the nurse caring for Eric perform a new intravenous procedure on him, but they do not provide the nurse with the policy that accompanies the procedure. What should the nurse do?

    1. Check the intravenous policies at the local hospital.
    2. Discuss the situation with the immediate nursing supervisor.
    3. Carry out the procedure but document that no policy existed.
    4. Contact the nursing practice consultant of the provincial/territorial nurses association.

scope in nsg. practice:

End of case 8

Case 9

Niomi Burr, 3 months old, is admitted to the pediatric unit for evaluation. Her presenting symptoms are weight loss and irritability. Niomi is diagnosed as having nonorganic failure to thrive. Her parents are young and inexperienced with childrearing.

QUESTIONS 46 to 50 refer to this case.

46. Which one of the following questions should the nurse ask to determine if the parents are facilitating Niomi's developmental task of "trust," as defined by Erikson?

    1. "What do you do when your baby cries?"
    2. "Do you provide your baby with a pacifier?"
    3. "What types of food do you feed your baby?"
    4. "What types of toys do you provide for your baby?"

47. The initial assessment data reveal that Niomi's urinary output is decreased, her anterior fontanel is sunken, and there is a decrease in her skin turgor. Which one of the following conditions is most likely indicated by these findings?

    1. Dehydration
    2. Hypervolemia
    3. Hyponatremia
    4. Water intoxication

48. Which one of the following actions by the nurse would promote Niomi's physical safety while she is in the hospital crib?

    1. Elevate Niomi's crib sides fully at all times.
    2. Position the crib mobile 15 cm above Niomi's face.
    3. Place a bubble top or net on the crib at the time of admission.
    4. Encourage her parents to position Niomi with her head on a pillow.

49. Niomi's parents state that they are afraid to bathe her because she is so small. Instead, they have just been wiping her with a cloth. What would be the best action by the nurse to promote Niomi's hygiene?

    1. Assist the parents to bathe Niomi during her hospitalization.
    2. Ensure that Niomi is bathed by staff during her hospital stay.
    3. Arrange to have follow-up supervision during Niomi's bath time at home.
    4. Have the parents demonstrate the bathing technique they have been using.

50. Which of the following behaviours by the nurse would best demonstrate a caring attitude toward Niomi's parents?

    1. Offer to feed Niomi when her parents seem tired.
    2. Recommend that Niomi's parents contact the social worker.
    3. Suggest to Niomi's parents that they stay with her 24 hours/day.
    4. Offer Niomi's parents reading material on effective parenting skills.

End of case 9

Case 10

Mrs. Goretti, 51 years old, has come to the Women's Health Centre because she thinks she may be starting menopause. During the initial meeting with the nurse, Mrs. Goretti states that she wants to know more about pills to control her hot flashes and ways to remain healthy. She also states that she has heard her friends talk about older women developing "brittle bones" and wants to know what she can do to prevent this.

QUESTIONS 51 to 56 refer to this case.

51. When interviewing Mrs. Goretti, which one of the following psychosocial assessments by the nurse would be most appropriate?

    1. Her religious affiliation and her marital status.
    2. Her cultural background and her feelings about aging.
    3. Her financial status and her husband's attitude toward her.
    4. Her socioeconomic status and the number of children she has had.

52. Mrs. Goretti tells the nurse that she has been having hot sweats every day and trouble sleeping at night. She has not had a menstrual period for 3 months, and states that she does not enjoy sexual relations now because it is painful and she is afraid of becoming pregnant. Which one of the following entries into the nursing notes is most appropriate?

    1. Amenorrhea for 3 months, fearful of becoming pregnant, complains of insomnia, painful coitus, and hot flashes.
    2. Amenorrhea for 3 months, hot flashes daily, insomnia, developing frigidity related to painful intercourse and fear of pregnancy.
    3. Amenorrhea for 3 months, hot flashes daily, loss of pleasure with coitus associated with dyspareunia and fear of pregnancy, insomnia.
    4. Amenorrhea for 3 months, anxious regarding conception, complains of insomnia, painful coitus, and hot flashes, fears becoming pregnant.

53. The physician has ordered transdermal estrogen replacement therapy for Mrs. Goretti. After 2 months she makes a follow-up visit to the Women's Health Centre. To assess Mrs. Goretti's response to the medication, which one of the following statements by the nurse would be most appropriate?

    1. "Have you had any side effects from the patch?"
    2. "How do you feel since you started using the patch?"
    3. "Has the patch controlled the problems you were having?"
    4. "Are you feeling better since you started using the patch?"

54. Mrs. Goretti states that at one time she found sexual relations pleasurable, but now she finds intercourse painful. Which one of the following statements best describes the client's health problem?

    1. Anxiety related to changing body image.
    2. Knowledge deficit related to changes in sexual patterns.
    3. Altered self-esteem related to changes in sexual patterns.
    4. Sexual dysfunction related to hormonal changes of menopause.

55. The nurse has developed an osteoporosis education plan with Mrs. Goretti. Which one of the following principles is most important for the nurse to apply when implementing the plan?

    1. The client must be ready to learn.
    2. A follow-up session with oral questioning will assist in evaluation.
    3. The teaching materials must be at the client's comprehension level.
    4. The client should be asked what she already knows about osteoporosis.

56. The nurse scheduled to care for Mrs. Goretti is new to the Women's Health Centre. How should this nurse prepare to care for Mrs. Goretti?

    1. Collect teaching pamphlets on menopause.
    2. Attend a workshop on aging and menopause.
    3. Talk to a co-worker who is going through menopause.
    4. Ask the client to share what she has learned about menopause.

End of case 10

Independent questions

QUESTIONS 57 to 99 do *not* refer to a case.

57. Mrs. Gans, an 80-year-old nursing home resident with stage 2 Alzheimer's disease, has been diagnosed with right lower lobe pneumonia. When the nurse offers Mrs. Gans her 16 00 antibiotic, the client shouts: "I'm not taking that! Get out!" Which of the following would be the most appropriate action by the nurse?

1. Leave the medication on the client's bedside table to allow her to take it when she is ready.
2. Using a firm tone of voice, reinforce to the client the need to take the medication.
3. Break open the capsules and place the powder in her food at dinner time.
4. Quietly leave the room and return 20 minutes later to offer the medication again.

58. A 16-year-old female visits her pediatrician's office. When in the examination room with the nurse, she states, "My boyfriend and I want to have sex. What kind of birth control method should I use?" Which of the following would be the most appropriate response by the nurse?

1. "You should ask the doctor. The doctor will give you the best advice."
2. "It isn't a good idea to be sexually active at your age. Let's talk about it."
3. "I'll tell you about the various methods and which ones also prevent sexually transmitted diseases."
4. "We will need the consent of one of your parents before I can give this information."

59. Which of the following practices should the nurse recommend to a prenatal class to reduce the risk of Sudden Infant Death Syndrome (SIDS)?

1. Place an electronic air filter in the infant's room.
2. Wrap the infant in a warm blanket.
3. Place the infant in the supine position for sleeping.
4. Place an infant monitor in the baby's room.

60. A nurse has just ended her shift on the pediatric unit where she participated in an unexpected and unsuccessful resuscitation of an 8-year-old girl. When a colleague asks the nurse how her day was, she bursts into tears and says: "I don't know if I can come back to work tomorrow!" How can the colleague best help the nurse cope with her feelings?

1. Tell the nurse that there probably was nothing else she could have done.
2. Tell the nurse that it is ok to cry and encourage her to speak about it.
3. Encourage the nurse to take a few days off to reflect on her feelings regarding the incident.
4. Reassure the nurse that she will be just fine and encourage her to go home and hug her children. *№ statement regarding children of the nurse*

61. Mr. Jonas will soon be discharged home from the cardiac unit. He indicates that he is concerned about his discharge because his home situation can be stressful. What strategy should the nurse employ to help him cope with stressful situations?

1. Encourage him to plan his daily activities.
2. Inform him that a nurse will visit him at home.
3. Reassure him that stress is normal and that he should just rest.
4. Have him practise a stress reduction method that he has found effective.

62. Mrs. Beaulieu has been admitted to the medical ward to rule out pulmonary tuberculosis. She has been placed in a negative pressure isolation room. What precautions should the nurse take when caring for Mrs. Beaulieu?

    1. Wear a disposable face mask whenever the nurse is in the client's room.
    2. Wear a disposable face mask only when in direct contact with the client.
    3. Wear a disposable face mask, gown and gloves whenever in direct contact with the client.
    4. Wear a disposable face mask, gown and gloves whenever the nurse is in the client's room.

63. A 21-year-old woman in active labour is admitted with contractions that are causing her distress. She requests something for the pain. What information should the nurse first obtain prior to providing analgesia?

    1. Frequency, duration, and intensity of contractions
    2. Presence and role of support person
    3. Preferred choice of analgesic
    4. Status of the amniotic membranes

64. Mrs. Smith is a gravida 3 para 2 at 33 weeks gestation. She has been hospitalized for 1 week with premature labour and will be discharged in the next two days. What should the nurse include in Mrs. Smith's discharge teaching plan?

    1. Provide client education pamphlets to Mrs. Smith and ask her to call back with any questions she may have.
    2. Show Mrs. Smith educational videos regarding the signs and symptoms of reccurrence and what to do for each situation.
    3. Identify what Mrs. Smith knows about premature labour and what she can do to help prolong the pregnancy.
    4. Evaluate Mrs. Smith's perception of what would be required of her if she were to be discharged to an antenatal home care program.

65. Mrs. James, 42 years old, is recovering from a total abdominal hysterectomy. The nurse notes during her assessment on the first postoperative day that the client is disoriented, hypotensive, and tachycardic. What is the most common cause of these symptoms?

    1. Hypothermia
    2. Hypovolemia
    3. Pain
    4. Anxiety

66. Mark, 4 years old, is monitored in the recovery room following a tonsillectomy and adenoidectomy. He is still unconscious, the oxygen saturation monitor has decreased from 99 to 94%, and gurgling sounds are heard. In addition to monitoring vital signs, what are the nurse's priority actions?

    1. Check placement of oral airway and position the child supine with head turned to the side.
    2. Check placement of oral airway and maintain the child in a prone position with head turned to the side.
    3. Remove oral airway and suction the back of the throat.
    4. Apply oxygen with a face mask and call the physician.

67. Mrs. Franklin, 46 years old, had a long leg cast applied 12 hours ago. She is complaining of unrelieved pain to the calf, inability to move her toes, and that her cast is too tight. What should the nurse initially do in this situation?

    1. Advise the physician.
    2. Reposition the extremity.
    3. Administer prescribed analgesic.
    4. Remove the cast.

68. On the second postoperative day after an abdominal perineal resection, Mr. Wilson complains that he feels bloated and would like to vomit. The nurse observes that the nasogastric tube is not draining. What should be the nurse's intervention?

    1. Check the tube for patency.
    2. Remove the tube and call the doctor.
    3. Administer the prescribed antiemetic.
    4. Apply gentle pressure to the upper abdomen.

69. The nurse admits a 55-year-old female with metastatic cancer to the liver. She is jaundiced, weak, and has marked ascites. Which of the following positions should the client be placed in when transferred to her bed?

    1. Semi-Fowler's
    2. High Fowler's
    3. Lithotomy
    4. Sim's lateral

70. Mrs. Taylor is recovering from an appendectomy. The nurse observes clear, watery drainage from the incision. What is this type of drainage?

    1. Serosanguinous
    2. Serous
    3. Sanguinous
    4. Purulent

71. Christian, 4 years old, weighing 15 kg, has been admitted for a bacterial respiratory infection. The pediatrician orders cefotaxime sodium (Claforan) 60 mg/kg/day, IV. What amount of medication should the nurse administer every 6 hours?

    1. 175 mg
    2. 200 mg
    3. 225 mg
    4. 250 mg

72. Mrs. Smith, 30 years old, with a history of asthma, arrives at the emergency in severe respiratory distress. She can barely speak. Auscultation reveals no air entry in the lower lobes. Which of the following ordered medical treatments should the nurse initiate first?

    1. IV normal saline
    2. Oxygen therapy
    3. Steroid medication
    4. Bronchodilator

73. Mrs. Stein, 30 years old, returns from a major surgery with morphine sulphate (Morphine) infusing via a Patient Controlled Analgesia (PCA) pump. The PCA is set to deliver 2 mg at 5-minute intervals with a maximum of 80 mg in 4 hours. On the first postoperative day, she says to the nurse, "I am afraid I am overdosing myself. I keep pushing the button every 15 minutes and I am still in pain." Which of the following interventions by the nurse will best assist Mrs. Stein to manage her pain?

    1. Assure her that antidote medication is available if she overdoses and encourage her to continue her use of the PCA pump.
    2. Reinforce to the client that she can push the PCA pump button as much as she wants if she has pain, without risk of overdose.
    3. Instruct her to stop using the PCA pump and have the physician reassess her needs.
    4. Give the client morphine sulfate (Morphine) 20 mg IM and reassess her level of pain in 30 minutes.

74. Mr. Daniels, 75 years old, is to be transfused with a unit of packed red cells. In order to safely administer the blood, what should the nurse do?

    1. Flush the blood infusion tubing with dextrose 5% in water (D5/W) intravenous solution.
    2. Verify with the client that the information on the blood product unit is correct.
    3. Assess vital signs, presence of chills, headache, or skin rash during the infusion.
    4. Upon completion of the transfusion, discontinue the intravenous infusion.

75. Mrs. Brunner, 86 years old, has worsening pneumonia. Her respiratory condition is deteriorating. What set of assessment data listed below confirms her condition?

    1. Tachypnea, use of accessory muscles, decreased air entry
    2. Tachycardia, barrel chest, nasal flaring
    3. Tachypnea, pursed-lip breathing, productive cough
    4. Increased anterior/posterior diameter, clubbing, wheezing

76. The nurse observes a newly admitted 25-year-old female client, with a diagnosis of paranoid schizophrenia, pacing up and down the hall, talking to herself in a loud, angry voice and making threatening gestures with her fists. To decrease the potential for the client to act out, which of the following interventions would be the most appropriate?

    1. Approach her with a relaxed posture and using a calm, low voice, acknowledge that she is upset.
    2. Prepare the p.r.n. medication which has been prescribed for her agitation.
    3. Gather several staff members to approach her as a group and ask what is upsetting her.
    4. Contact the physician to ask for an order to place the client in locked seclusion.

77. Mrs. Jones has just been diagnosed with an inoperable brain tumor. Her physician has suggested to her to stop all treatments. She becomes angry and uncooperative and when approached she yells: "Stay away from me. I just want to die." How should the nurse respond to the client?

    1. "I know how you feel. I will leave you alone for a while."
    2. "Since you are upset why don't we discuss something else today."
    3. "You are upset. I am available to talk whenever you are."
    4. "Let me give you a pill to calm you down and I'll come back later."

78. Mrs. Black, 69 years old, is admitted for a fractured femur. She will undergo an open reduction and internal fixation. Mrs. Black asks when she will be able to walk again. How should the nurse respond?

    1. "You should be allowed to walk with assistance three days after your surgery."
    2. "You may be up walking with assistance the first day after your surgery."
    3. "Your doctor will write the order as soon as he examines you after the surgery."
    4. "When you no longer feel pain and are well enough to walk on your own."

79. Two registered nurses are working the night shift on a surgical floor with a student nurse. While one of the registered nurses is on break, a client requests his pain medication. The nurse knows that she will have to waste 0.5 ml of Demerol solution when drawing up the ordered dosage. Which actions by the nurse demonstrate compliance with procedures for disposal of narcotics?

    1. She will draw up the medication, discard the wastage, and ask the RN who is on break to co-sign the wastage when she returns.
    2. She will draw up the medication, ask the student nurse to witness, and co-sign the wastage.
    3. She will draw up the medication, place the unused portion in the narcotic cupboard, and ask the RN to witness and co-sign wastage on her return from break.
    4. She will call the nursing supervisor or an RN from another floor to come to witness and co-sign the wastage.

80. Mrs. Parker, a 64-year-old female with Parkinson's disease, has been agitated, uncooperative, and having difficulty sleeping. The physician orders lorazepam (Ativan) 20 mg, p.o., b.i.d.. What should the nurse do initially when she reads this order?

    1. Transcribe the order and administer the medication.
    2. Clarify the order with the physician.
    3. Ask the physician to change the route to sublingual.
    4. Notify pharmacy and request delivery as soon as possible.

81. The nurse smells alcohol on a colleague's breath. Later in the evening, the colleague asks for assistance giving an injection to a client. The nurse observes that her colleague's hand is shaking, she is unable to landmark safely, and does not appear to be able to focus on the task. What is the nurse's best intervention?

    1. Stop her colleague from giving the injection and from providing client care. Inform the supervisor and ask for replacement staff. Document observations of her colleague's behaviour.
    2. Allow her colleague to give the injection after guiding her hand to the correct injection site. Monitor and document her colleague's behaviour for the remainder of the shift. Advise other staff of her concerns.
    3. Tell her colleague in a firm voice to stop what she's doing and give the injection for her. Ask to speak to her colleague outside the client's room. Confront her colleague and ask if she has been drinking.
    4. Take the needle and syringe out of her colleague's hands and give the injection. Suggest to her colleague that she sit at the nursing station and only answer the phone for the remainder of the shift.

82. Sharon, 15 years old, has just delivered her first baby. The father of the baby does not wish to be involved. During her postpartum hospital stay, Sharon expresses uncertainty regarding her desire to keep the baby. What should the nurse do in this situation?

    1. Request that the hospital chaplain discuss adoption options with Sharon.
    2. Organize a family conference with Sharon, her parents, and the father of the baby.
    3. Suggest that Sharon delay her decision until the community health nurse visits.
    4. Refer Sharon to a social worker or community agency for immediate counselling.

83. The community nurse at a First Nations Friendship and Health Centre is developing interventions related to the high incidence of diabetes identified in this community. The nurse's goal is to prevent diabetic complications. What would be the nurse's most appropiate initial intervention?

    1. Set up home visits to assess the clients' current health practices related to diabetes management.
    2. Invite elders, the health centre's dietitian, and First Nations home support workers to a meeting.
    3. Arrange transportation of clients to the health centre's diabetic education program.
    4. Develop a reading package including Canada's Food Guide, menu plans, and information about diabetes.

84. An occupational health nurse is implementing a series of lifestyle programs for employees. Which of the following programs is an example of health promotion?

    1. Flu vaccination clinic
    2. Blood pressure screening
    3. Cholesterol testing
    4. Workshop on Canada's Food Guide

85. There has been an increase in accidents causing head injuries among students who ride bicycles in the community. The nurse at the local elementary school wants to promote the use of helmets. Considering the principles of teaching and learning, which of the following would be the most effective strategy for the nurse to promote helmet use?

    1. Send a letter home to the parents emphasizing the importance of wearing helmets.
    2. Recommend to the school principal that cyclists without helmets not be allowed on the school grounds.
    3. Give the students a pamphlet containing statistics on head injuries and helmet use.
    4. Organize a meeting with concerned parents, teachers, and students to discuss the issue.

86. The nurse is teaching a group of new mothers how to care for a newborn with a fever. Which of the following recommendations should the nurse include in her teaching?

    1. "If the fever persists for more than 3 days, you should contact your pediatrician."
    2. "A massage with an alcohol based product will quickly help to reduce the temperature."
    3. "Take the infant's temperature by placing the digital thermometer under the armpit."
    4. "Acetaminophen (Tylenol) and Acetylsalicylic acid (Aspirin) are effective for reducing fevers in infants."

87. While teaching a prenatal class, the group questions the reliability of lactation as a method of contraception. How should the nurse respond to their questions?

    1. "The choice of relying on lactation is entirely up to you and your partner."
    2. "Lactation is a highly reliable choice of natural family planning."
    3. "The use of oral contraception is the recommended choice during lactation."
    4. "The use of lactation as a birth control method is not reliable."

88. During prenatal classes for teenage expectant mothers, they share their concerns over their ability to breastfeed. They question their ability to "make milk that will help their baby grow, as they are still growing." How should the nurse respond?

    1. "If you are capable of becoming pregnant you are capable of breastfeeding."
    2. "Because you are still growing, you may not be able to produce enough milk for your baby."
    3. "Your body should be able to produce the milk your baby will need."
    4. "Your ability to produce milk is limited but partial breastfeeding is something you might want to consider."

89. A day care centre has recently had a number of children and staff members who have had bacterial gastroenteritis. The administrator has asked the nurse to provide the staff with information on preventing the recurrence of this problem. What health practice should the nurse recommend?

    1. Isolating the children who have loose stools.
    2. Handwashing after using the toilet or changing a diaper.
    3. Disinfecting toys with an antibacterial solution.
    4. Ensuring children's immunizations are up to date.

90. The nurse is conducting a series of Healthy Heart lectures at the local Senior Centre. While discussing the hazards of smoking and the benefits of quitting, several of the audience members verbalize concerns about their ability to "kick the habit." Which of the following responses by the nurse is the most supportive?

    1. "It is difficult. You may have some relapses, but over time your health will benefit."
    2. "You know how bad smoking is for your heart and you should quit for your own health."
    3. "If you can't stop smoking, you will just have to work harder on reducing other health risk factors."
    4. "You should discuss this with your physician because smoking is an important health risk factor."

91. Mrs. Elmy is visiting her 3-year-old daughter on the pediatric unit. She has to bring her 6-month-old son when she visits. She asks the nurse if she should continue the immunization program for her son because she wonders if he will "catch something more easily if he gets his shots." What recommendation should the nurse give Mrs. Elmy?

    1. "Wait until your daughter has recovered before you continue with your son's immunization."
    2. "There is no need to interrupt your son's immunization at this time."
    3. "You should ask your family doctor's advice on this matter."
    4. "You should find out if there have been any recent communicable illnesses in your neighbourhood."

GO TO NEXT PAGE

92. Mr. Kellior, 72 years old, is admitted to the emergency department with an acute onset of shortness of breath, chest pain and anxiety. The initial assessment is as follows: RR 22, cyanosis of the lips and nailbeds, and O2 saturation of 83%. What should be the nurse's immediate action?

    1. Place him on cardiac monitor.
    2. Place him on supplementary oxygen.
    3. Complete the physical assessment.
    4. Request a 12-lead electrocardiogram.

93. During a figure-skating practice, 11-year-old Kelly Lewis falls and fractures her leg. In the first 8 hours following surgery, what complication should be of most concern to the nurse?

    1. Postoperative infection
    2. Deep vein thrombosis
    3. Fluid imbalance
    4. Compartment syndrome

94. Mr. Tran, 80 years old, has undergone a radical prostatectomy and is receiving morphine sulphate (Morphine) via a patient controlled analgesia (PCA) pump. What PCA specific assessment should the nurse complete first ?

    1. The client's understanding of how to use the PCA pump
    2. The rate and quality of respiration
    3. The programmed parameters of the PCA pump
    4. The client's level of pain

95. The nurse is caring for Melissa, a 17-year-old ballet student. She was admitted to hospital a week ago with a 12% deep partial thickness burn to her right hip and thigh, suffered when she fainted and fell against a hot radiator. The nurse notes that Melissa has been sending most of her meal trays back barely touched. What should the nurse do?

    1. Tell Melissa that the dietitian has calculated her nutritional requirements and she needs to eat everything that is on her tray.
    2. Explain to Melissa that a diet high in calories and protein has been ordered by the doctor in order to promote healing.
    3. Share with Melissa her observations that she is not eating and explore the reasons.
    4. Discuss with Melissa the option of using total parenteral nutrition to promote healing.

96. Surinder, 10 years old, is admitted to the pediatric unit. His pediatrician orders methylphenidate hydrochloride (Ritalin) p.o., 0.3 mg/kg/day in equal divided doses at 10 00 and 22 00. He weighs 40 kilograms. What dosage should the nurse administer at 10 00?

    1. 3 mg
    2. 6 mg
    3. 12 mg
    4. 24 mg

97. Rosa, 12 years old, is hospitalized for vomiting and diarrhea. The order on the chart reads: Dextrose 5% in 0.9% Saline, IV at 100 ml/hr. The nurse finds the infusion pump infusing at a rate of 200 ml/hr. Which of the following actions should the nurse take initially?

    1. Turn off the infusion pump.
    2. Reduce the infusion rate to 100 ml/h.
    3. Verify the intravenous order.
    4. Complete an incident report.

98. Mr. Camper, 68 years old, who has a history of asthma, is recovering from hip surgery. While doing his morning care, the nurse notes: moderate dyspnea, pallor, and an audible wheeze. Which of the following doctor's orders should the nurse implement first?

    1. Lorazepam (Ativan) 1 mg, SL, q 8h, p.r.n.
    2. Salbutamol (Ventolin) by nebulizer q 4h, p.r.n.
    3. Nitroglycerine (Nitrolingual) 1-2 sprays repeated q 5min x 3, p.r.n.
    4. Acetaminophen with codeine 30mg (Tylenol 3) 2 tabs q 4-6 h, p.r.n.

99. Mr. Quinlan, 52 years old, weighing 90 kg, arrives at the emergency with severe right lower back pain radiating to right flank. The physician orders meperidine (Demerol) 50 mg, IM, q 3-4h, p.r.n. Forty five (45) minutes after the administration of the medication, the client's level of pain has not changed. What should the nurse do?

    1. Explain to the client that the peak effect of the medication has not been achieved.
    2. Request an order for an increase in the dosage of meperidine.
    3. Administer the next dose as soon as the p.r.n. time parameters allow.
    4. Explain to the client that it is too soon to administer his next dose of medication.

End of independent questions

Case 11

Mrs. Kirsh is a 70-year-old woman who has been admitted to hospital because she has developed signs of acute renal failure. She is in the oliguric phase, and complains of nausea and drowsiness.

QUESTIONS 100 to 105 refer to this case.

100. The specific gravity of Mrs. Kirsh's urine is low. Lab data reveal hyponatremia and hyperkalemia. What further assessment of Mrs. Kirsh should the nurse conduct?

    1. Listen to her chest.
    2. Note signs of hypovolemia.
    3. Observe for postural hypotension.
    4. Assess signs of fluid volume deficit.

101. Which one of the following nursing actions should be a priority in planning care for Mrs. Kirsh?

    1. Encourage oral fluid intake.
    2. Weigh the client before meals.
    3. Leave the side rails up at all times.
    4. Encourage independence in activities of daily living.

102. Which one of the following nursing interventions should be a priority for the nurse to perform with Mrs. Kirsh hourly?

    1. Turn and position.
    2. Measure urinary output.
    3. Promote deep breathing.
    4. Check for signs of edema.

103. The nurse answers Mrs. Kirsh's call light to find her looking very agitated and exclaiming, "Nurse, look what's happened; am I bleeding to death?" She is holding a kidney basin which is full of blood. Which one of the following responses by the nurse would be most appropriate?

    1. "Wait right there and I'll get the doctor at the desk."
    2. "What were you doing that could have caused this?"
    3. "It can be pretty scary when you're bleeding. Let me help you."
    4. "No, you're not bleeding to death. It always looks worse than it is."

104. A float nurse, unfamiliar with the unit, is assigned to care for Mrs. Kirsh. What should the charge nurse do to ensure that any noticeable changes in Mrs. Kirsh's condition are reported?

    1. Check the float nurse's charting.
    2. Verify the float nurse's assessment.
    3. Review with the float nurse what should be assessed and reported.
    4. Ask the nurse working in the next room to be available to the float nurse.

105. Mrs. Kirsh has been making satisfactory progress and her IV has been discontinued. What intervention should the nurse take to ensure that Mrs. Kirsh's food and fluid needs will continue to be met?

    1. Provide milkshakes t.i.d.
    2. Ensure her privacy during meals.
    3. Encourage a high-calorie breakfast.
    4. Measure her intake and output, and give her water between meals.

End of case 11

Case 12

Mr. Paul Krantz is an 18-year-old college student. He has a complete spinal cord lesion at T1 and a closed-head injury as a result of a diving accident which happened 1 week ago. He has remained unconscious since his admission.

QUESTIONS 106 to 110 refer to this case.

106. The nurse and Mr. Krantz's mother are bathing him. Which one of the following approaches by the nurse would best promote a helping relationship between the nurse, Mr. Krantz, and Mr. Krantz's mother?

    1. Address Mr. Krantz, saying, "Paul, your mom is here helping to wash you."
    2. Quietly say to Mr. Krantz's mother, "You must be worried about your son's recovery."
    3. Speak slowly and clearly to Mr. Krantz, saying, "Please just try to open your eyes for your mom."
    4. Reduce auditory stimulation and whisper to Mr. Krantz's mother, "Why don't you give him a back rub?"

107. Mr. Krantz has been started on total parenteral nutrition (TPN). During a bag change, the bag containing the solution of amino acids is inadvertently punctured by the spike on the tubing. Which one of the following interventions by the nurse would best maintain the TPN infusion?

    1. Tape the hole with sterile, waterproof tape and continue the infusion.
    2. Slow the infusion and wait for a new bag to be delivered from the pharmacy.
    3. Continue the infusion with Dextrose 10% until a new bag is available from the pharmacy.
    4. Increase the rate of the lipid infusion until a new bag of amino acids can be administered.

108. Which one of the following nursing actions would be most effective in promoting circulation in Mr. Krantz's lower limbs?

    1. Apply resting splints to both legs.
    2. Flex and extend the client's ankles q 2h.
    3. Administer warm packs to both calves t.i.d.
    4. Elevate the foot of the client's bed 15 cm with a slight knee bend.

109. In managing the physical environment, which one of the following measures should the nurse perform to promote safety for Mr. Krantz?

    1. Keep the lights in the client's room dimmed.
    2. Ensure the client's bedsheets are free of wrinkles.
    3. Turn the client from prone to supine positions q. 2h
    4. Have the curtains around the client's bed open at all times.

110. During the night shift, the nurse caring for Mr. Krantz and three other spinal cord injured clients becomes involved in the care of an unstable client and cannot attend to the other clients. What should the nurse do to ensure a safe practice environment?

1. Document the situation, and provide a rationale for the decisions made.
2. Advise the nursing supervisor of the situation and request assistance on the unit.
3. Leave the unstable client in a recovery position and proceed to perform care for the other clients.
4. Delegate the practical nurse/nursing assistant to stay with the unstable client while the nurse attends to the other clients.

End of case 12

Independent questions

QUESTIONS 111 to 130 do not refer to a case.

111. An 85-year-old client wishes to use a hot water bottle for management of arthritic pain at home. The nurse is teaching the client's family how to use the hot water bottle. How should the nurse respond when the family asks about proper temperature of the water and timing?

1. "Fill the hot water bottle from a boiling kettle and keep it on as long as it stays warm."
2. "Fill the hot water bottle from a boiling kettle and keep it in place for 30 minutes."
3. "Fill the hot water bottle with warm tap water and keep it in place for 30 minutes."
4. "Fill the hot water bottle with warm tap water and keep it on as long as it stays warm."

112. Mr. Kowalski, 65 years old, is receiving intravenous antibiotic therapy every 12 hours. He is receiving his medication through an intermittent infusion device (saline lock) located in his left hand. Which of the following statements regarding intermittent infusion devices is correct?

1. Flushing the device with 10 ml of normal saline q 4h.
2. When flushing, positive pressure should be applied on the plunger when withdrawing the needle.
3. The device should be replaced every 24 hours.
4. Cleanse the injection port with an iodine preparation prior to each infusion.

113. Mr. Kant, 72 years old, is 12 hours post-op following a transuretheral resection of the prostate. He has a three-way system for continuous bladder irrigation. Four hours after beginning working with Mr. Kant, the nurse notes that the colour of the drainage in the tubing has become darker with shreds of clots. What is the most appropriate measure to implement at this time?

1. Ask Mr. Kant to remain in bed.
2. Milk the drainage tubing.
3. Manually irrigate the catheter.
4. Increase the flow rate of the irrigation solution.

114. Mrs. Anderson, 66 years old, had a repair of a perforated bowel 2 days ago. The nurse notes that the doctor has left an order to remove the nasogastric tube. What should influence the nurse's decision to carry out this order?

    1. This is standard procedure 2 days after bowel surgery, so removal is appropriate.
    2. The tube is uncomfortable and should be removed as soon as possible after surgery.
    3. There is minimal drainage and bowel sounds have returned, so the tube is unnecessary.
    4. The longer the tube stays in place, the greater the potential for gastric infection.

115. Mrs. Baxter is receiving chemotherapy drugs through a central venous catheter inserted into the right subclavian vein. During the assessment, the nurse notes that the client is dyspneic and cyanotic, has hypotension and a weak rapid pulse. She says she has pain in her chest and shoulder. Based on these findings, what complication is the client most likely experiencing?

    1. Circulatory overload
    2. Infiltration
    3. Infection
    4. Air embolism

116. Mr. Fontaine, 65 years old, and his wife live in a seniors apartment complex with 24-hour nursing service. Mr. Fontaine falls and fractures his hip. After treatment in hospital, he is ready to go home. The client must be assisted in maintaining hip precautions. How can the discharge nurse best ensure continuity of his rehabilitation?

    1. Send a pamphlet that outlines hip precautions to the nurse on site at the complex.
    2. Telephone the nurse on site at the complex and give a complete report.
    3. Ensure the hospital physiotherapist has reviewed hip precautions with the client and his wife.
    4. Complete a referral to the community physiotherapist and arrange for a home visit.

117. Mrs. Hodges, 49 years old, is being discharged from the coronary care unit following admission for unstable angina and angioplasty. She understands that her smoking habit is a significant risk factor in cardiovascular disease. Which of the following options would be the most appropriate in assisting the client to quit smoking?

    1. Tell her to consult her friends who have stopped smoking.
    2. Advise her to gradually reduce the number of cigarettes smoked daily.
    3. Provide her with information on smoking cessation programs in the community.
    4. Request that her cardiologist order a nicotine patch.

118. Which of the following is the nurse's primary goal in establishing a bladder retraining program for an incontinent client?

    1. Client limits fluid intake to 1 litre a day.
    2. Client voids small amounts every hour.
    3. Client is familiar with the procedure for self-catheterization.
    4. Client utilizes a variety of techniques to postpone the urge to void.

119. Mr. Dunnery, 28 years old, has had numerous admissions to the psychiatric unit due to bipolar disorder. At the most recent admission, his wife tells the nurse that she cannot convince him to take his medication and that he has been drinking heavily. She and their two young children are no longer able to cope with his aggressive behaviour. She feels very guilty about being relieved when he is in hospital and asks for help. How should the nurse respond to this situation?

   1. Assure the wife that the client will stay on the psychiatric unit as long as possible, so that the family will have respite from this situation.
   2. Ask the client's wife if she would like to discuss her situation with the social worker.
   3. Refer the mother and her children to the local family crisis centre so that they can be relocated.
   4. Tell the client's wife that she will arrange for the community mental health worker to visit the home more frequently.

120. A client on the unit asks the nurse about the possiblity of having her cat visit. The hospital has no policy on pet visitation. What should the nurse do in response to the client's request?

   1. Call the physician and request an order for the visit.
   2. Consult the unit manager regarding the client's request.
   3. Call the client's family and ask them to bring in the cat.
   4. Explain to the client that the hospital would not allow a visit because it does not have a policy regarding pet visits.

121. Which of the following actions by the nurse best demonstrates application of principles of aseptic technique while changing a dressing?

   1. Prepares the dressing tray in a clean utility room.
   2. Cleanses the wound, moving from the centre of the wound outward.
   3. Removes the old dressing and then puts on clean gloves.
   4. Changes the Montgomery straps/tie tapes every two days.

122. The nurse in a long-term care agency enters a client's room and sees Linda, an unregulated health care provider, administering nitroglycerine spray (Nitrolingual) to the client. Linda tells the nurse that the client had been complaining of chest pain, and yesterday, she noted how quickly the chest pain was relieved once the spray was applied. How should the nurse intervene in this situation?

   1. Take the client's vital signs and tell the client not to allow Linda to give him any medication.
   2. Compliment Linda, telling her that she demonstrated good judgment in this situation.
   3. Inform Linda that it is the nurse's role to administer medications, not the unregulated health care provider's, and report the incident.
   4. Clarify the unregulated health care provider's job description with the supervisor.

123. While providing care to an unconscious client, the nurse notices that her coccyx is reddened and tender, but the skin is not broken. What would be the nurse's most effective intervention to promote healing and prevent further tissue damage?

   1. Communicate with the health team to ensure that the area is massaged frequently to improve circulation.
   2. Ensure adequate nutritional intake to promote healing of the damaged tissue.
   3. Use powder on the area with morning care and as necessary throughout the day.
   4. Arrange for the client to be placed on a pressure relief mattress.

124. A client in labour, fully dilated and pushing, is screaming in pain. The nurse approaches the husband in the waiting room and asks him to assist his wife to focus. He says, "It is not part of our culture for the husband to be with his wife during childbirth." How should the nurse respond?

    1. "Women in labour do much better when their husbands are present."
    2. "Is there someone else you can call to be with her?"
    3. "She really needs you right now."
    4. "I understand, I will be able to help your wife."

125. Mr. Mobi, 69 years old, is hospitalized for investigation of a mass on his liver. Mr. Mobi says to the nurse, "I feel uncomfortable praying when there are other men in the room." How should the nurse respond?

    1. "I am sorry you feel uncomfortable. Maybe you can pray while the other men are sleeping."
    2. "I am sorry for your discomfort. Would you like to discuss this with a chaplain?"
    3. "I recognize your concern. Would you like to be transferred to a private room?"
    4. "I understand your discomfort. I can arrange for a quiet place to be available to you."

126. Sara, 17 years old, has come to the health clinic requesting oral contraceptives. The nurse and Sara review the action, dosage and adverse effects of oral contraceptives. Following the teaching session, Sara takes a 3-month supply. What response by Sara indicates that teaching was effective?

    1. "I will take the first pill on day five of my period."
    2. "If I experience breast tenderness, I should stop the pill immediately."
    3. "I will only smoke during my period when I am not taking the pill."
    4. "If I should miss a day, I should begin a new cycle of the pill."

127. Natalie, 4 years old, is suffering from pediculosis and impetigo. Which one of the following statements would be most appropriate for the community health nurse to use with Natalie's family when teaching them about infection control?

    1. "Natalie must be isolated to prevent the spread of infection."
    2. "You must prevent further excoriation of Natalie's skin, to keep secondary infections from occurring."
    3. "It is important not to be overprotective and restrict Natalie. This could stifle her emotional growth."
    4. "Natalie's skin needs to be kept clean and dry. She needs to wear clean clothes daily and have her sheets and pillow case changed."

128. Upon observing seizure activity in Mrs. Simpson, which one of the following nursing actions should be taken initially?

    1. Set up suction equipment.
    2. Restrain Mrs. Simpson to prevent injury.
    3. Stay with Mrs. Simpson while calling for help.
    4. Reassure Mrs. Simpson by using gentle touch.

129. Mrs. Dubinski, 76 years old, is being discharged from hospital following a total replacement of her right hip. Which one of the following actions should the nurse take to plan for a discharge that is compatible with the client's <u>lifestyle</u>?

    1. Teach the client's family about positioning and transferring techniques.

    2. Find out what types of resources are available to the client and her family.

    3. Arrange for a community health nurse to visit the client at home on a regular basis.

    4. Interview family members to determine their availability for providing home care for the client.

130. Jordan, 6 years old, is being discharged in a hip spica cast extending down one leg. Which one of the following adaptations must be made to meet his needs when he returns home?

    1. His parents will have to rent a hospital bed.

    2. His mother will need to buy him loose-fitting clothes.

    3. Arrangements will have to be made to rent a wheelchair.

    4. A home care worker will be required to assist with turning him.

End of independent questions

End of Book 1

Canadian Registered Nurse Examination

CANDIDATE NUMBER

SIGNATURE

Book 2

Test Form 01920

Read the instructions and sample questions inside the front cover

CANADIAN NURSES ASSOCIATION
ASSOCIATION DES INFIRMIÈRES ET INFIRMIERS DU CANADA

INSTRUCTIONS

A) TESTING TIME AND MATERIAL

You will have three and one-half hours to work on this test. The starting and finishing times will be announced and you will be advised when there are 30 and 15 minutes working time remaining. If at any time you have any questions about what you should do, raise your hand and an invigilator will assist you.

You will be advised whether you may leave the examination room if you finish the test before the time is up. You must stop working when the signal is given. An invigilator will check your test book and answer sheet before you leave.

Clear your desk of all materials except your identification card, answer sheet, test book, pencils, and eraser. Do not fold, bend, or tear your answer sheet, as this could affect the scoring of your test.

B) ANSWER SHEET

Complete the identification portion of your answer sheet. Print your name, date of birth and date of the examination. Print and fill in the test form number (from the cover of your test book).

If you have a candidate label provided with your identification card: detach the label from the identification card and place the label in the appropriate location on the answer sheet. Do **not** fill in the information to the right of the candidate label unless the candidate label is incorrect. **If you do not have a candidate label:** fill the oval corresponding to the language of writing, print your candidate number and writing centre code, and fill the corresponding oval for each digit.

Be sure the mark you make for each answer is black, fills the oval, and contains the number corresponding to the number of the answer you have chosen. Do **not** fill in more than one oval for a question or you will get no credit for it. Erase **completely** any answer you wish to change and mark your new choice in the correct oval. An incomplete erasure may be read incorrectly as an intended answer. Do not press too heavily on your pencil or you may damage the answer sheet.

Note that the questions on the answer sheet are numbered in columns. There are fewer questions in the test book than there are numbers on the answer sheet.

Make no stray marks on the answer sheet; they may count against you. You may use the margins of the test book for any scratch work, but you will *not* get credit for anything you write in the test book.

C) TEST BOOK

Sign your name on the line on the cover of this book and copy your candidate number into the appropriate boxes. If you do not have a candidate number, **print** your name under your signature.

Read each question carefully and choose the answer that you think is the **best** of the four alternatives presented. If you cannot decide on an answer to a question, go on to the next one and come back to this question later if you have time. Try to answer all questions. Marks are not subtracted for wrong answers. If you are not sure of an answer, it will be to your advantage to guess. It will probably be best to start at the beginning of the test and work through the questions in order.

This examination contains a number of experimental questions being tested for future use. Your answers to these questions will **not** count toward your score. Because you will not be able to tell which questions are experimental, you should do your best on all questions, but do *not* spend too much time on any question.

The questions in the examination may be presented in nursing cases or as independent questions. The context of some cases may seem similar to others in your test book. This reflects current practice where a nurse may have to care for different clients with similar problems. Each case, however, tests different nursing content. The sample case on the next page shows the types of questions used. Correct answers are blackened in the ovals on the right.

Sample Case

Sally Bowman, 15 years old, is 3 months pregnant. She has been referred to the community health nurse for prenatal counseling and teaching. During the interview with the nurse, Sally states that she smokes about 20-25 cigarettes per day.

QUESTIONS 1 to 5 refer to this case.

1. Sally tells the nurse that it was not her idea to visit the nurse and that she is unsure about returning. Which one of the following responses by the nurse best demonstrates a helping attitude?

 1. "Would you like me to arrange for you to see another nurse?"
 2. "Some of your friends must be very worried about you."
 3. "I wonder what ideas you have for how we can work together?"
 4. "If getting here is difficult, I can arrange to see you wherever it is convenient for you."

  ①②●④

2. At the end of their interview, Sally tells the nurse that she thinks she will continue to smoke. Which one of the following adolescent developmental tasks should the nurse identify as the most likely barrier to smoking cessation?

 1. Accepting a changing body image
 2. Establishing a value system
 3. Striving for independence and maturity
 4. Seeking social stability

  ①②●④

3. Which one of the following statements by the nurse best reflects the appropriate application of the principles of communication?

 1. "Are you aware of how harmful smoking is to both you and your baby?"
 2. "Let's talk about getting you enrolled in our Stop Smoking Program."
 3. "Can you tell me how long you have been smoking and why you started?"
 4. "Tell me how you feel about the effect of smoking on your baby."

  ①②③●

4. At Sally's next visit 1 month later, she tells the nurse that she has been able to decrease the number of cigarettes she smokes to 5 -10 per day. Which one of the following long-term goals is Sally most likely working toward?

 1. A decrease in the incidence of neonatal respiratory disorders
 2. A decrease in the risk of fetal growth retardation
 3. An increase in potential fetal iron stores
 4. A decrease in the incidence of fetal congenital anomalies

  ●②③④

5. Pat is a colleague who is observing the nurse's developing relationship with Sally. Pat remarks to the nurse, "You seem to be spending a great deal of time with Sally. Are you sure this isn't affecting your other clients?" Which of the following actions should the nurse take first in response to Pat's comments?

 1. Present Pat's concerns to another colleague for validation.
 2. Re-evaluate the relationship with Sally and the possible need for change.
 3. Clarify Pat's comments and ask her to elaborate on her concern.
 4. Verify with the other clients their level of satisfaction with the care provided.

  ①②●④

End of sample case

DO NOT OPEN YOUR TEST BOOK OR BEGIN WORKING UNTIL THE SIGNAL IS GIVEN TO DO SO

Case 13

Mr. Lallor, 20 years old, is admitted to the psychiatric unit with a diagnosis of schizophrenia. On his arrival, he presents with hallucinations and delusional ideas. His appearance is neglected and his affect inappropriate. Mr. Lallor is accompanied by his mother, with whom he lives, and his sister. According to his sister, Mr. Lallor was verbally aggressive to his mother when she tried to get him to take his medication. During the week following admission, the nurse meets with Mr. Lallor, his mother, and his sister.

QUESTIONS 1 to 6 refer to this case.

1. Which one of the following statements would help give the nurse a better understanding of Mr. Lallor's delusional ideas?

    1. They are an indicator of the client's intellectual capacity.
    2. Their purpose is to reduce the client's problems and stress.
    3. They are a help in understanding the causes of the client's illness.
    4. They reflect a change in the client's personality.

2. Taking into account Mr. Lallor's potential for violence, how could the nurse best help him and his family prevent violent incidents?

    1. Observe relations between the client and family members.
    2. Convince the family that the client must leave the home.
    3. Help the client and his family identify their respective needs.
    4. Plan the client's care with other family members.

3. The nurse notes that Mr. Lallor is demonstrating low self-esteem and is becoming isolated. Which one of the following points must the nurse consider first when encouraging Mr. Lallor to participate in a support group?

    1. His fear of intimacy
    2. His hallucinations
    3. His trust in the nurse
    4. His medications

4. When revising Mr. Lallor's care plan, how can the nurse help improve his self-esteem?

    1. By organizing activities in which there is a lot of interaction
    2. By encouraging him to leave his room to prevent isolation
    3. By suggesting tasks that he can perform successfully
    4. By complimenting him regularly

5. Mr. Lallor expresses the desire to learn to live on his own. What would be the first step in planning his teaching plan?

    1. Set learning objectives for the client.
    2. Encourage the client to participate in a support group.
    3. Make an inventory with the client of the skills he would like to develop.
    4. Give the client a list of what he needs to know.

6. When planning Mr. Lallor's discharge, what method should the nurse use to help him perform his daily hygiene care?

    1. Tell him how important it is to be clean.
    2. Ask his family to remind him to wash himself in the morning.
    3. Help him prepare a reminder system that he can use at home.
    4. Plan with him how to keep a diary of his daily activities.

End of case 13

Case 14

Mrs. Billing, 27 years old, and her husband are expecting their first baby. They visit the community health centre.

QUESTIONS 7 to 12 refer to this case.

7. During the couple's first visit to the prenatal clinic, what data collection method is most appropriate?

    1. Assessment of vital signs and body mass
    2. Health assessment and physical examination
    3. Blood and urine tests
    4. Assessment of the labour and delivery plan

8. During the second visit to the clinic, Mrs. Billing informs the nurse of the following: fatigue, loss of appetite, drowsiness and lack of energy. The nurse notes that the blood test results show a decrease in hemoglobin and hematocrit levels. What should the nurse do for Mrs. Billing?

    1. Discuss the possibility of a rest period during the day.
    2. Plan with the client an increase of iron intake in her diet.
    3. Recommend that the client take a leave of absence from work.
    4. Encourage the spouse to perform household chores.

9. To avoid injuries associated with the change in a pregnant woman's centre of gravity, which one of the following measures should the nurse suggest to Mrs. Billing?

    1. Wear support stockings.
    2. Elevate the legs when sitting.
    3. Wear flat shoes.
    4. Reduce physical activities.

10. In the second trimestre, Mrs. Billing experiences difficulty resting because of lower back pain. Which one of the following recommendations by the nurse will most effectively help relieve Mrs. Billing's pain?

    1. Place feet in dorsiflexion.
    2. Maintain good posture.
    3. Avoid crossing her legs.
    4. Perform pelvic tilts.

11. Mrs. Billing talks to the nurse about her difficulty in sleeping because of urinary frequency. What should the nurse do?

    1. Recommend reducing her fluid intake by half.
    2. Suggest replacing fluids with solids.
    3. Recommend reducing her fluid intake in the evening.
    4. Reinforce the importance of being well hydrated.

12. At 22 weeks gestation, Mrs. Billing tells the nurse that she is experiencing constipation. What suggestion should the nurse make?

    1. Make a change in her physical fitness program.
    2. Stop taking the iron supplement because it accentuates this problem.
    3. Take a stool softener that she can obtain over the counter at the pharmacy.
    4. Increase the fluid and fibre intake in her diet.

End of case 14

Case 15

The nurse in a community health centre is responsible for establishing the health profile of students in a secondary school. The school principal tells her that drug use among students is apparently increasing, resulting in increased absenteeism.

QUESTIONS 13 to 17 refer to this case.

13. What must the nurse do initially to introduce an intersectoral cooperation project to deal with the drug issue in the school?

    1. Conduct a survey of members of the school personnel.
    2. Facilitate a support group consisting of parents, students and health professionals.
    3. Invite those involved in the school and community to participate in an awareness-raising meeting.
    4. Discuss this issue with the nurses in the community health centre.

14. How does the nurse demonstrate respect for values and behaviours to students engaging in high-risk behaviour?

    1. By sharing her fears with them
    2. By allowing them to speak freely
    3. By imposing limits on them
    4. By being sensitive to their needs

15. Following an information session on the consequences of drug use, Julie, a Grade 12 student, tells the nurse about her concern regarding her friend Sarah's recent use of cocaine. She asks the nurse not to speak to her friend about it for fear of damaging their friendship. What should the nurse do in these circumstances?

    1. Respect Julie's request.
    2. Speak to Sarah's parents about the matter.
    3. Consult Sarah's teachers.
    4. Discuss with Julie the purpose of informing the nurse of this matter.

16. During the consultation process, the nurse encourages Sarah in her initiatives to return to good health. Which one of the following comments indicates that Sarah is moving toward self-management of her health situation?

    1. "I am able to handle this by myself."
    2. "I am receiving help from my friends."
    3. "I visit my physician regularly."
    4. "I am participating in support group meetings."

17. At her last meeting with Sarah, what should the nurse include in a process to prevent relapses?

    1. Develop a stress management plan.
    2. Limit social encounters.
    3. Encourage family activities.
    4. Suggest keeping a diary of her activities.

End of case 15

Case 16

Mr. Rourke, who is 34 years old, married and the father of two children, is hospitalized for depression. He has been unemployed since the factory closed. He says that he feels hopeless and is worried about his future.

QUESTIONS 18 to 23 refer to this case.

18. Which one of the following replies should the nurse make when Mr. Rourke says, "My life is hopeless now. I can't find the courage to go on"?

    1. "It is often by taking one step at a time that we succeed in overcoming our difficulties."
    2. "What would help you regain your interest in life and help you to adapt?"
    3. "You know, depression is now a treatable illness."
    4. "What you are telling me is that you no longer feel like living."

19. What behaviour indicates most clearly to the nurse that Mr. Rourke is at risk for suicide?

    1. He asks to see his wife.
    2. His mood improves.
    3. He says that he would like to settle his financial problems.
    4. He states that he is not interested in participating in a group.

20. Mr. Rourke's condition stabilizes after a few days and he is invited to participate in a support group. Which nursing measure most effectively promotes Mr. Rourke's integration into the group?

    1. The nurse invites him to listen to comments expressed by the resource person who is talking about depression.
    2. The nurse encourages him to explain to the members of the group what people with depression experience.
    3. The nurse prevents him from leaving the group although he is crying and refuses to say what the problem is.
    4. The nurse encourages him to share his own experiences and to listen to the experiences of the group members.

GO TO NEXT PAGE

21. At mealtime, Mr. Rourke's behaviour changes abruptly. He speaks in a loud voice, gestures, becomes impatient easily, and threatens to strike another client. What should the nurse do initially to help Mr. Rourke?

    1. Have him eat alone in his room and cancel his leave privileges.
    2. Explain to him the importance of respecting the unit's rules.
    3. Give him the opportunity to return to his room, remain with him, and allow him to express himself.
    4. Request assistance from the security guards, take him to his room, and apply physical restraints.

22. What should the nurse do to facilitate adaptation for a client with a dissociative identity disorder?

    1. Confront the client when he adopts defensive behaviours.
    2. Offer the client the opportunity to express his feelings by reflecting his emotions.
    3. Involve the family as soon as possible to help the client decide on his treatment plan.
    4. Encourage the client to interact with his family, other clients, staff members, and his visitors.

23. A week after his arrival, Mr. Rourke is becoming increasingly isolated. He attempts to injure himself and clearly informs the nurse of his intention to attempt suicide on the unit. What must the nurse do first to prevent Mr. Rourke from injuring himself?

    1. Move him to a private room to allow him to rest.
    2. Remove any personal effects with which he could injure himself.
    3. Administer a sedative and observe for therapeutic effect.
    4. Telephone his spouse and ask her to remain with him.

End of case 16

Case 17

Mrs. Riker, 18 years old, is a nursing student and has been complaining for 1 week of abdominal cramps accompanied by diarrhea (10 to 15 bowel movements a day), weight loss, and rectal bleeding. She has painful oral ulcers and is pale. A provisional diagnosis of colitis has been made. She is to undergo a colonoscopy and laboratory tests. She appears anxious about the colonoscopy and the provisional diagnosis, and questions the nurse.

QUESTIONS 24 to 29 refer to this case.

24. Which one of the following explanations by the nurse best describes this diagnostic examination?

    1. "An iodized contrast medium is injected into the bowel to visualize it."
    2. "A radiopaque catheter is introduced into the bowel to assess the status of the colon."
    3. "A rectal tube is inserted to visualize the status of the bowel."
    4. "A flexible tube is inserted in the rectum to visualize the large bowel mucosa."

25. Following admission, what data should the nurse consider as a priority for Mrs. Riker's care plan?

    1. Signs of weight loss
    2. Factors triggering diarrhea
    3. Effects of chronic pain on the client's lifestyle
    4. Skin turgor

26. A fibre-restricted, high-protein diet is ordered for Mrs. Riker. Why does Mrs. Riker need this type of diet?
    1. She has oral ulcers and this type of diet will lessen oral pain.
    2. Her health condition is causing weight loss and this diet will bring about a gradual weight gain.
    3. This diet provides food that is digested in the upper part of the jejunum and does not stimulate intestinal secretion.
    4. This diet contains suitable electrolytes and will meet the client's nutritional and energy requirements.

27. Mrs. Riker is receiving salazopyrin (Sulfasalazine) 500 mg. t.i.d. Which one of the following manifestations indicates to the nurse that the medication is having the desired therapeutic effect?
    1. The electrolytic imbalance is decreasing.
    2. She has less diarrhea.
    3. Periods of insomnia are less frequent.
    4. She is no longer anemic.

28. The nurse explores with Mrs. Riker coping strategies to deal with her health problem. What should the nurse recommend to Mrs. Riker?
    1. Increase her knowledge about the health problem.
    2. Entrust her care management to her parents.
    3. Consult a psychiatrist to express her concerns.
    4. Take stress management courses.

29. Which one of the following comments by the nurse would most likely encourage Mrs. Riker to communicate with other persons who have inflammatory bowel disease?
    1. "Here is a list of community resources that are available."
    2. "I am going to refer you to a specialized service."
    3. "Sharing experiences can reduce the feelings of isolation and anxiety."
    4. "I suggest that you attend some lectures on inflammatory bowel disease."

End of case 17

4

Case 18

Mr. Sander has had Alzheimer disease for 3 years. He is 81 years old and lives with his 72-year-old wife. He takes little part in his care and is confused at times. When the nurse asks Mrs. Sander what worries her most, she replies that her husband has been sleeping poorly for the past 8 days, and often wakes at night. He roams around inside the house and wants to go outside. She is greatly disturbed by his behaviour, which prevents her from sleeping. Mrs. Sander states that she is tired and cries easily. However, she prefers to care for her husband herself and has refused any help until now. The home care nurse meets with Mr. and Mrs. Sander.

QUESTIONS 30 to 34 refer to this case.

30. Which of the following aspects should be a priority for the nurse?

1. The family's relationships with health professionals
2. The problems with activities of daily living
3. Communication between family members
4. The couple's social isolation

31. The nurse modifies the Sander family's plan of care. Which of the following measures takes priority among the family's needs?

1. Mobilizing the family's external resources
2. Discussing with Mrs. Sander the impact of her spouse's illness on her own health
3. Teaching Mrs. Sander how to care for her spouse when he roams around the house
4. Explaining to Mrs. Sander the importance of taking rest periods

32. The nurse suggests prevention strategies to Mrs. Sander, who is worried about her husband roaming at night. Which of the following suggestions by the nurse would reduce the risk of accidents?

1. Install an alarm bell on the bedroom door.
2. Ensure adequate lighting in the house.
3. Administer sleeping medication to Mr. Sander before he retires.
4. Ensure that someone stays with him.

33. Mrs. Sander states that she is very tired and is beginning to doubt her ability to care for her husband. Which one of the following responses most effectively provides the support Mrs. Sander needs?

1. "Perhaps it would be preferable to place your husband in a nursing home."
2. "Let me find someone to help you."
3. "How do you feel about the possibility of taking some respite periods?"
4. "Do you know that most informal caregivers feel powerless at certain times?"

34. The family physician suggests to Mrs. Sander that she apply to have her husband placed in a long-term care facility. She refuses and tells the nurse that it is too early to make this decision. How can the nurse advocate for Mrs. Sander?

1. Take steps with Mrs. Sander to examine all options for maintaining home care.
2. Seek help from nurses at the community health centre.
3. Encourage Mrs. Sander to express her beliefs about her role as caregiver.
4. Call the family physician to learn the reasons for his recommendation.

End of case 18

Case 19

Mrs. Tyson, 47 years old, has been diagnosed with breast cancer and undergoes a modified radical mastectomy.

QUESTIONS 35 to 40 refer to this case.

35. During the preoperative assessment, Mrs. Tyson tells the nurse she is worried about her two young adult daughters' well-being and future health. She asks the nurse what advice she should give her daughters for early breast cancer detection. What should the nurse recommend?

1. Her daughters should have a mammogram every two years.
2. Her daughters should have an annual Pap test.
3. Her daughters should practise breast self-examination every month.
4. Her daughters should have a pelvic exam every year.

36. The nurse notes that in the last 12 postoperative hours, Mrs. Tyson has had 3000 ml of IV fluid infused and has voided twice for a total 250 ml. What should be the nurse's first intervention?

1. Reduce the IV flow rate.
2. Palpate the bladder area.
3. Obtain a urine culture.
4. Assess for fever and chills.

37. Mrs. Tyson refuses chemotherapy treatments for her breast cancer. She states that "the loss of my breast was the end of my life anyway, so why bother?" How should the nurse respond?

1. "How can you feel this way when you have a family that cares for you?"
2. "You are upset. Tell me why you feel the loss of your breast is the end of your life."
3. "You'll be all right. These treatments are usually very effective in your type of cancer."
4. "Let's talk about it when you are feeling better. I will be back later."

38. Mrs. Tyson is extemely depressed and feels that even though she has strong faith, her wonderful God has abandoned her. The nurse develops a nursing care plan to address the client's spiritual distress. How should the nurse assist the client in this situation?

1. Call the client's spiritual adviser.
2. Recommend to the client that she continue to read her religious books.
3. Explore with the client what has given her life meaning in the past.
4. Advise the client that her God is loving and everything has a meaning.

39. Mrs. Tyson is being prepared for discharge. She asks the nurse why she must continue her arm exercises at home. What is the most important reason for the nurse to encourage these exercises?

1. Exercise will facilitate the development of collateral circulation.
2. Exercise is an effective measure to reduce postoperative pain.
3. Scarring at the operative site is reduced by these exercises.
4. Arterial lymphatic drainage will be facilitated with exercise.

GO TO NEXT PAGE

40. Mrs. Tyson's wound has a drainage device that requires emptying every shift. Which of the following statements should guide the nurse's use of gloves while emptying the drainage device?

    1. Gloves can be used between clients if they are intact.
    2. Long fingernails and rings compromise the safety of the gloves.
    3. Gloves should only be used if the client exhibits signs of wound infection.
    4. When frequent handwashing is impossible, gloves provide protection.

End of case 19

Case 20

Mr. Nelson, 66 years old and weighing 100 kg, is accompanied by his family to the emergency department. He has had a headache, left-sided weakness and mild confusion for the past 2 hours. He has difficulty answering some of the nurse's questions on initial examination.

QUESTIONS 41 to 46 refer to this case.

41. Which of the following methods would be most appropriate in obtaining this client's history?

    1. Ask questions that the client can answer with a yes or no.
    2. Obtain the client's previous health records.
    3. Involve the client's family in obtaining information.
    4. Allow the client to rest and complete the history at a later time.

42. Mr. Nelson indicates to the nurse that his headache is getting worse and that he is experiencing increased weakness in his left arm and leg. His vital signs are as follows: T 37 °C, P 88, R 16 and BP 200/124 mmHg. A nitroglycerin IV drip is started. Which data should the nurse use to evaluate the effectiveness of this intervention?

    1. Size of pupils
    2. Blood pressure
    3. Severity of the headache
    4. Hand grips

43. When the nurse returns to the emergency department from lunch, Mr. Nelson is lying in a supine position on the stretcher staring into space. His color is dusky, his respirations are loud and stertorous, and his left arm is shaking involuntarily. Which of the following would be the nurse's priority intervention?

    1. Shake him and give oxygen by mask.
    2. Place him in high Fowler's position and raise the siderails.
    3. Assess his airway and call for assistance.
    4. Insert an oral airway and give him oxygen by mask.

44. Mr. Nelson is admitted for further investigation of a suspected transient ischemic attack and is scheduled for a (CT) scan of his head. His left-side weakness persists. Which of the following measures should the nurse use to safely transfer the client to the medical imaging department?

    1. Assist the client to sit at the side of the bed, then to stand and pivot into a wheelchair.

    2. Place a stretcher next to the bed and ask the client to move onto the stretcher.

    3. Request help from other staff members and use a transfer board to slide the client onto the stretcher.

    4. Use a transfer belt and assist the client to pivot into a wheelchair.

45. Mr. Nelson is placed on a calorie restricted diet. He states that he is unsure about his ability to continue with the diet at home. Which of the nurse's responses would be the most supportive?

    1. "You have done well in the hospital so you should be able to continue at home the same way."

    2. "You have made some significant changes already; what problems do you anticipate at home?"

    3. "Would you like me to have the dietitian bring you more information?"

    4. "Once you get home you will feel better so don't worry about that now."

46. The nurse prepares a discharge teaching plan for Mr. Nelson which includes his dietary modifications. Which of the following interventions will best assist the client in maintaining his diet?

    1. Inform the client that he may call the community dietitian at any time for help.

    2. Schedule a follow-up appointment with the hospital dietitian.

    3. Arrange for a representative of a local weight loss support group to visit him.

    4. Suggest he use his hospital menus to plan his meal at home.

End of case 20

Case 21

Mr. Mann is a 65-year-old semi-retired fisherman who lives on a converted tugboat moored in the local harbour. His daughter, Diane, telephones the community nurse because her father has been having problems with his urination. She adds that he isn't fond of doctors and he does not have a telephone.

QUESTIONS 47 to 51 refer to this case.

47. What should be the nurse's response to the daughter?

    1. Recommend the father increase his fluid intake and drink cranberry juice.

    2. Inform the daughter that older men often have changes in their bladder function.

    3. Advise the daughter to make an appointment with a physician.

    4. Arrange for a time to meet with the daughter and father on the boat.

48. Mr. Mann is diagnosed with cancer of the prostate and undergoes a radical prostatectomy. The day after surgery, Mr Mann looks pale and the nurse notes that his hemoglobin result is 76 g/dl. What should be the nurse's first intervention?

    1. Assess the client for symptoms of low hemoglobin.

    2. Call the laboratory to do a blood group and screen.

    3. Advise the surgeon of the hemoglobin result.

    4. Review the client's chart to determine his blood loss since surgery.

GO TO NEXT PAGE

49. Two days after his surgery, Mr. Mann appears downcast and quiet and he tells the nurse that he misses his dog. What would be the nurse's most supportive intervention at this time?

    1. Remind him that it will only be a few more days before he sees his dog.
    2. Call the daughter and ask her to come and visit her father.
    3. Invite him to the TV lounge to meet other clients.
    4. Investigate the possibility of having the dog visit the client.

50. Mr. Mann will be discharged soon and the nurse is reviewing follow-up instructions when Mr. Mann interjects with "I guess I am less of a man now." How should the nurse respond?

    1. "Mr. Mann, you are going to be just fine and you have a family that cares for you."
    2. "You may be over-reacting but talk to the doctor at your follow-up appointment ."
    3. "There are information pamphlets about sexual function after surgery I can give you."
    4. "What have you been told that makes you feel this way?"

51. Mr. Mann's daughter arrives to pick him up and is worried about him returning to his boat. What information should the nurse emphasize to the community care nurse who will care for Mr. Mann?

    1. The client's postoperative status.
    2. The client lives on a boat.
    3. The client has no telephone.
    4. The client's concerns about his sexuality.

End of case 21

Case 22

Mr. Hannah, 28 years old, has been HIV positive for 5 years. Recently, he has been admitted to the hospital with a confirmed diagnosis of Pneumocystis Carinii and is placed in reverse isolation. For the past year, he has been on zidovudine (AZT) 100 mg 5 times a day.

QUESTIONS 52 to 57 refer to this case.

52. Mr. Hannah says to the nurse, "I thought I was supposed to get better when I went on AZT. I have had more colds this year than I have ever had. They are more severe and harder on me. Is it the effect of the AZT?" What is the nurse's best response?

    1. "Maybe you should be taking less AZT or a different medication altogether. Let's talk to your doctor about that."
    2. "AZT actually helps to prevent infections and should not be the cause of frequent colds."
    3. "AZT works on slowing the progression of HIV. Your susceptibility to colds has more to do with the effects of HIV on your immune system."
    4. "Maybe it's not working because of the times you are taking it. Are you taking it as prescribed? "

53. While Mr. Hannah's partner is visiting him, he tells the nurse, "We have always wanted to have a tattoo, so when I get out of here, we are going to get matching tattoos." What response by the nurse would be the most appropriate?

    1. "Your skin will not heal well right now; therefore, getting a tattoo is not a good idea."
    2. "It sounds like you and your partner want to live life to its fullest."
    3. "People are usually sorry a few years after they get a tattoo. Are you sure you want one?"
    4. "Be careful that the tattoo parlor uses sterile equipment."

54. Mr. Hannah tells the nurse that he does not want to have any heroic measures, such as resuscitation, carried out while he is in the hospital. What should be the nurse's response?

    1. "I know that you are not feeling well right now, but you are much too young to be talking about dying."
    2. "I will write it on your chart and make sure that the nurses will respect your wishes."
    3. "Why don't we talk about what you mean by resuscitation."
    4. "You should really think this through. New promising discoveries for HIV are made every day."

55. Mr. Hannah tells the nurse that he has noticed people seem to avoid coming into his room and that he is lonely. What strategy should the nurse use to provide support to the client?

    1. Explain to him the reason he is isolated is due to his susceptibility to infections.
    2. Explain to him that people don't come into his room because they are afraid of getting HIV.
    3. Ask him if any of his family can come to the hospital to keep him company.
    4. Spend time talking with him during and between care activities.

56. Which of the following measures should the nurses implement when caring for Mr. Hannah to protect themselves from infection?

    1. Wear a mask when in the client's room.
    2. Wear a gown when in the client's room.
    3. Use disposable plates and cutlery for the client's meals.
    4. Wash hands after contact with the client.

57. While in hospital, Mr. Hannah has been using an air bed for reddened bony prominences and his skin has not broken down further. He fears his skin will break down at home if he does not have an air bed. His source of income is a disability pension and he says he can't afford to buy one. Which of the following actions by the nurse best considers the client's situation?

    1. Contact the psychologist to assist the client with his anxiety.
    2. Suggest that a slightly underinflated air mattress would work just as well as the air bed.
    3. Contact the social worker to interview the client and his partner about financial resources.
    4. Insist that he really does need an air bed at home.

End of case 22

4

Independent questions

QUESTIONS 58 to 99 do *not* refer to a case.

58. How should the nurse interact initially with a new female client who frowns, rarely smiles, and replies in monosyllables?

1. Greet the client using her first name and ask her if she is ready for breakfast.
2. Greet the client using her first name, introduce herself, and suggest that the client take a bath to relax.
3. Greet the client using the client's name and ask if she has any concerns.
4. Greet the client using the client's name, introduce herself, and inform the client of her observations.

59. The parents of Karin, 13 years old, consult the school nurse. They inform the nurse that they are having problems enforcing effective discipline methods. What should the nurse suggest?

1. Prepare a schedule of activities for Karin.
2. Punish Karin each time she is disobedient.
3. Guide Karin in making decisions.
4. Give Karin responsibilities associated with privileges.

60. The nurse wants to encourage Grade 9 students to adopt a healthy lifestyle. Which one of the following statements best reflects the principles of health promotion?

1. Daily exercise results in improved concentration for studying.
2. A healthy diet results in increased life expectancy.
3. A good lifestyle helps prevent contagious diseases.
4. A healthy lifestyle helps increase well-being.

61. Which one of the following teaching strategies should the nurse use to meet the learning needs of a 68-year-old client who must undergo electroconvulsive therapy?

1. Provide him with some information leaflets that he can read about the therapy.
2. View a video on the therapy with him and his wife.
3. Give him a research article on the effects of the treatment.
4. Ask him to invite his wife to take part in a support group and discuss it with him subsequently.

62. Which of the following factors should the nurse first consider when determining whether a client can change his lifestyle?

1. Physical and intellectual ability
2. Readiness
3. Life experience
4. Environment

63. Which of the following research findings should the nurse explain to a mother whose 18-year-old daughter regularly abuses alcohol?

    1. "It is a problem that most often affects unemployed women in their thirties."
    2. "Alcohol abuse results directly from the father's alcohol use."
    3. "A link exists between social attitudes and alcohol consumption."
    4. "Alcohol abuse is a sign of a personality disorder."

64. What should the nurse do to facilitate physical activity among a group of seniors with osteoporosis, who like to go for a daily walk outside?

    1. Encourage them to comply with safety measures when going outside.
    2. Teach them to maintain appropriate body alignment while walking.
    3. Encourage them to perform range-of-motion exercises before walking.
    4. Explain the importance of raising their feet before walking to promote circulation in the limbs.

65. What is the best way for the nurse to promote safe sexual practices in a group of adolescents?

    1. Provide condoms.
    2. Encourage abstinence.
    3. Teach ways to prevent pregnancy.
    4. Teach safe sex practices.

66. Mr. Parks, 50 years old, is admitted to hospital for a myocardial infarction. He smokes 20 cigarettes a day and drinks 120 ml of rye every weekend. The nurse makes the following assessment: BP 170/140 mmHg, RR 22, T 37 °C, and HR 90. He is 1.72 m tall and weighs 130 kg. Which risk factors should the nurse consider when assessing Mr. Parks's health status?

    1. Sedentary lifestyle and stress
    2. Hypertension and tachycardia
    3. Excess weight and smoking history
    4. Excessive alcohol consumption and age

67. Mr. Biddle, a client with AIDS, is in the terminal phase. What should the nurse do to reduce the risks of disease transmission?

    1. Wear a mask when providing direct care.
    2. Wear an isolation gown when in contact with the client.
    3. Wear gloves when handling body fluids.
    4. Wear protective glasses when in contact with urine.

68. During a home visit to Mr. Bennet, 65 years old, the nurse notices that despite episodes of angina, he continues to smoke, he is inactive, and his diet is high in saturated fats. What should the nurse do to help Mr. Bennet understand the importance of adopting a healthy lifestyle?

    1. Ask him about the reasons for his behaviour.
    2. Discuss his needs in relation to his lifestyle.
    3. Start a new care process.
    4. Register him in a smoking cessation program.

69. What information should the nurse give to reduce the risks of toxicity in a client who has to take Lithium at home after a lengthy hospitalization?

    1. The importance of salt and liquids in the diet
    2. The importance of taking missed doses
    3. The importance of monthly blood tests
    4. The importance of knowing when to stop the medication

70. Which one of the following strategies should the nurse use to gather data when she suspects that an 19-year-old man is substituting alcohol for food?

    1. Conduct a health assessment.
    2. Consult the dietician.
    3. Ask the client to keep a daily food diary.
    4. Check the client's blood alcohol.

71. Heather, 15 years old, has run away from home and is in a large city for the first time. One month after her arrival, she visits a shelter for the homeless and asks the help of the community nurse. She tells the nurse that she fears she has contracted HIV. What data should the nurse collect as a priority to assess whether Heather's fears are founded?

    1. Nutritional status and quality of sleep
    2. Alcohol and medication use
    3. Sexual activity and drug use
    4. Medical history and blood tests

72. Mr. Tran is discharged from hospital. He returns home in constant pain, which he manages to control with medication. Which one of the following statements shows the home care nurse that Mr. Tran is putting into practice the teaching he received on pain control?

    1. He can explain the process of self-injecting his medication.
    2. He confirms that his wife fully understands how to administer his medication.
    3. He can demonstrate how to self-inject his medication.
    4. He says that he used the same medication before his hospitalization.

73. Mrs. Watts, 60 years old, has had abdominal surgery. What should the nurse do to facilitate optimal ventilation and respiration for Mrs. Watts?

    1. Have her change position and perform respiratory exercises every four hours.
    2. Have her sit on the side of the bed and perform deep breathing and coughing.
    3. Have her sit in Fowler's position and administer oxygen therapy.
    4. Administer an analgesic and have her ambulate frequently.

74. Mr. Johnson has had abdominal surgery, and there is considerable yellowish discharge at the incision site. What should the nurse do to promote re-establishment of skin integrity at the incision site?

    1. Clean the incision every day and cover it with a dressing.
    2. Clean the incision when necessary and leave it exposed to the air.
    3. Clean the incision frequently and change the dressing.
    4. Clean the incision at the client's request and leave it exposed to the air.

75. The physician orders 75 mg of meperidine hydrochloride (Demerol) for Mr. Dent. An ampul of meperidine hydrochloride contains 100 mg in a quantity of 2 ml. What dosage should the nurse administer to Mr. Dent?

    1. 0.6 ml
    2. 0.7 ml
    3. 1.5 ml
    4. 1.6 ml

76. Jack, 14 years old, is hospitalized because of a knee infection. What should the nurse do to ensure safe administration of medications?

    1. Check the physician's order and ask Jack to state his name.
    2. Check the dosage calculation and Jack's identity card on the wall.
    3. Check the medication three times during preparation and Jack's identity bracelet.
    4. Check the frequency of administration of the medication and Jack's room number.

77. An occupational health nurse in a local company meets with Mr. Dunlop, who is having problems adapting to the company's reorganization. How should the nurse respond to Mr. Dunlop's manager when he asks for information about Mr. Dunlop's condition and his ability to function in his job?

    1. "Why don't you talk directly to Mr. Dunlop about your concerns?"
    2. "Would you like me to arrange a meeting for you with Mr. Dunlop to discuss your concerns?"
    3. "I could begin by providing you with some information about what Mr. Dunlop is experiencing."
    4. "I think that for the time being, Mr. Dunlop needs a little rest and some stability in his job."

78. Mrs. Bell is receiving an epidural anesthetic and is hypotensive. What should the nurse do as a priority?

    1. Place pillows under the client's back.
    2. Administer oxygen at 2 L/min by nasal cannula.
    3. Increase the IV rate.
    4. Position the client in supine position.

79. Ms. Leming, 66 years old, is experiencing perceptual dysfunctions on the left side secondary to a cerebrovascular accident 2 weeks ago. How can the home care nurse best adapt Ms. Leming's care?

    1. By placing all useful objects on the client's right.
    2. By having the client wear non-skid shoes for walking.
    3. By teaching her to turn her head and systematically scan her entire environment.
    4. By ensuring that she has glasses that are well adjusted to her vision.

80. The home care nurse visits a 80-year-old client whose wife died 6 months ago. He only goes out to do his groceries and to go to the bank. What should the nurse do to facilitate the client's social interaction?

    1. Prepare, with the client, a list of activities that interest him.
    2. Explain that the quality of social relations is more important than their frequency.
    3. Recommend that he register for personal growth and self-development courses.
    4. Invite the client's family to visit him more often and accompany him when he goes grocery shopping or to the bank.

81. Three months ago, Mr. Marshall, 55 years old, experienced a cerebrovascular accident resulting in left hemiparesis. During a visit to his home, where he lives with his spouse, the nurse notices that, despite some progress, Mr. Marshall does not seem very motivated to continue with the rehabilitation started with the occupational therapist. After collecting data, the nurse concludes that Mr. Marshall is depressed. How should the nurse intervene?

    1. Refer the client to a psychiatrist.
    2. Refer the client to another occupational therapist.
    3. Help the client verbalize his feelings.
    4. Encourage the client to perform more exercises.

82. A nurse in a psychiatric hospital is concerned about what families of hospitalized clients are experiencing. What should the nurse do to ensure the health and well-being of the families?

    1. Propose to hospital management that families be visited at home.
    2. Establish a telephone support service so families can express their feelings.
    3. Propose the creation of a specialized centre to study family behaviour.
    4. Offer to meet with families regularly during hospitalization of a family member.

83. What should the nurse do to respect and promote the autonomy of an 18-year-old, pregnant client who wants to learn how to modify her diet because of her pregnancy?

    1. Give her a copy of Canada's Food Guide and ask her to fill out the weight grid.
    2. Prepare with the client a health evaluation of her daily food intake.
    3. Suggest that the client take a vitamin supplement and increase her water intake.
    4. Consider organizing a workshop on diet and inviting the client to attend.

84. The nurse has great difficulty in distancing herself from the care of her client when she leaves work. What would be the best strategy for the nurse to adopt?

    1. Recognize that she is too compassionate.
    2. Request that the client be assigned to another nurse.
    3. Share her concerns with the client.
    4. Confide in a colleague whom she trusts.

85. A client being treated for cancer of the breast has consented to participate in a clinical trial for a new drug. She is experiencing side effects which could be related to the drug and wants to withdraw from the trial. She is concerned that the doctor will be angry if she does so. She asks the nurse what to do. How should the nurse respond?

    1. "I'm sorry, I can't tell you what to do. It has to be your decision."
    2. "Your doctor is used to people withdrawing from studies. He won't be angry."
    3. "Don't worry about the doctor being angry. It is your right to withdraw from the study."
    4. "You need to discuss your concerns with your doctor. Would you like me to stay while you do?"

86. Mrs. Alio has recently been admitted to a long-term care facility. She does not interact with other residents, looks sad, and has been observed crying. How should the nurse intervene at this time?

    1. Ask other residents to visit her.
    2. Take her to organized activities such as singing.
    3. Speak with her about her feelings.
    4. Suggest an antidepressant to the physician.

87. Which of the following health trends should the nurse use as a basis to develop a health promotion program?

    1. The use of safety equipment, such as bicycle helmets and seat belts, has reduced the incidence of injury and death.
    2. Many people have adopted healthy eating habits, but not as many regularly exercise.
    3. More people recognize that a balanced diet reduces the risk of developing cancer.
    4. More people are engaging in activities such as running and meditating, contributing to a sense of well-being.

88. A client diagnosed several months ago with type 1 diabetes has come to the nursing clinic for assistance in managing his diabetes. He is homeless and has just been able to secure work. He is motivated to carry through with the teaching plan. What would be the nurses' best approach to assist the client to implement the plan?

    1. Provide him with information on how to obtain supplies needed to manage his diabetes.
    2. Review all diet information stressing the importance of eating balanced meals.
    3. Observe him drawing up and giving his insulin.
    4. Review complications that can occur if the diabetic plan is not followed.

89. What should be the nurse's first step in developing an occupational health program designed to decrease worker absenteeism in a large factory?

    1. Identify factors contributing to absenteeism in this factory.
    2. Assess the factory employees' willingness to participate.
    3. Implement a healthy lifestyle campaign for factory employees.
    4. Evaluate the use of safety devices on the factory floor.

90. What is the best approach by the nurse to teach a group of 3-year-old children hygienic behaviours?

    1. Explain to the group why they need to wash their hands after using the toilet.
    2. Ask the parents to wash their children's hands after they use the toilet.
    3. Hang a picture by the sink which shows a child washing his hands.
    4. Demonstrate handwashing while the children wash their hands at the same time.

91. A nurse working in an extended care facility is caring for a resident who has dementia with aggressive episodes in which he strikes out at caregivers. What should the nurse do to avert aggressive behaviour by the client?

    1. Restrain the resident's arms so he cannot strike out.
    2. Try reasoning with the resident to thwart the behaviour.
    3. Give the resident sedation to stop the aggression from developing further.
    4. Withdraw from the setting, giving the resident quiet time to settle.

4

92. A 9-month-old child is admitted to the emergency having suddenly developed a cough. When an attempt is made to assess the child's respiratory status, she begins to cry loudly. Which assessment should the nurse perform first?

    1. Respiratory rate
    2. Heart rate
    3. Chest sounds
    4. Skin colour

93. The nurse is bathing a client who tires easily. She requires a chest assessment, an abdominal dressing change, vital signs, an IV site change, and IV medications. Which interventions should the nurse perform while doing the client's bath?

    1. Take vital signs and administer IV medications.
    2. Complete chest assessment and change abdominal dressing.
    3. Change IV site and complete chest assessment.
    4. Change abdominal dressing and change IV site.

94. A 28-year-old client, weighing 80 kg, underwent an appendectomy yesterday. He was given morphine sulfate (Morphine) 15 mg IM, 45 minutes ago. He states that his pain is still severe. Which action by the nurse is most appropriate?

    1. Administer another dose of Morphine.
    2. Explain that the medication has not reached its full effect.
    3. Record in the chart that the analgesic was not effective.
    4. Use complementary measures, such as relaxation techniques.

95. What should be the nurse's response when a client asks why massage relieves pain associated with muscle tension?

    1. "It decreases the perception of pain."
    2. "It inhibits the conduction of pain."
    3. "It increases the threshold for pain."
    4. "It enhances the tolerance for pain."

96. Mr. Smith, 68 years old, is suspected of being infected with hepatitis B virus. What precautionary measures should the nurse take while caring for Mr. Smith?

    1. Avoid direct physical contact while assisting with activities such as bathing and defecating.
    2. Wear gloves and mask while providing physical care requiring any type of bodily contact.
    3. Wear gloves and goggles or eye glasses if contact with bodily fluids is anticipated.
    4. Wear gloves, mask, and a gown when performing a venipuncture or establishing an IV.

97. A 55-year-old client with benign prostatic hyperplasia is scheduled for a retropubic prostatectomy. Following a consultation with his physician, he asks the nurse if his surgery will cause impotence. What should be the nurse's response?

    1. "You should not worry. Your sexual functioning will be unchanged."
    2. "Some clients experience erectile dysfunction, but it is hard to predict."
    3. "If you are really concerned, you should have discussed this with your doctor."
    4. "You seem worried? Were you planning to have more children?"

98. Nausea and vomiting are the second most common symptoms in palliative care clients. Which of the following interventions by the nurse will best assist the palliative client and his family to reduce these symptoms?

    1. Teach them to use imagery during the symptoms.
    2. Explain how to anticipate and prevent the symptoms by using prescribed medications.
    3. Recommend that they modify the diet and provide small frequent meals.
    4. Instruct them to avoid activity when any sign of nausea occurs.

99. The parents of an 8-year-old boy have just learned that their son died two hours ago. The nurse finds the distraught parents in the hallway expressing guilt for not being with their son at the time of his death. What should the nurse do in meeting the parents' emotional needs?

    1. Take them to their son's room and help them come to terms with his death.
    2. Notify the supervisor and request her to come and stay with the parents.
    3. Arrange for pastoral care to come and talk to the parents.
    4. Provide privacy, offer to stay with them, and allow them to vent their feelings.

End of independent questions

Case 23

Camp Trillium is a summer residential camp for children in active treatment for cancer or who have had cancer. The ages of campers range from 8 to 16 years. The leadership team includes a director, nurse, program director, water safety director, dietician, on-call oncologist, and counsellors.

QUESTIONS 100 to 105 refer to this case.

100. During the initial leadership team meeting, the camp director asks the nurse if she would spend an hour a day at the waterfront so the lifeguard can have her lunch break. How should the nurse respond?

    1. Consent to the request so that the leadership team can commence the summer on a positive note.
    2. Clarify that the nurse's role is to provide health care and that lifeguarding duty is beyond the scope of nursing practice.
    3. Suggest that the lifeguard could shorten her work day and not have a lunch break.
    4. Suggest that the members of the leadership team take turns replacing the lifeguard during her lunch break.

101. During the team meeting, the program director and the camp director engage in a heated discussion about the time of "lights out" (bedtime) for campers. What action by the nurse best reflects the principles of conflict resolution?

    1. Call for a vote so that the meeting can proceed.
    2. Ask the directors to identify the issues on which they agree.
    3. State that an early bedtime is best because sleep is essential to good health.
    4. Allow the discussion to run its course so that feelings can be vented.

102. An 8-year-old male camper comes to the nurses' office crying and states, "I must have been bit by lots of mosquitoes last night cause I can't stop scratching. And I'm so hot." The nurse notices that the boy has a runny nose, mild fever, and a pruritic rash on his trunk. Which of the following actions by the nurse would be most appropriate?

    1. Suggest that the child swim in the lake to ease the itching, and apply calamine lotion to the rash afterward.

    2. Give the child a bottle of insect repellent to protect him from further insect bites. Comfort him with a cold drink of juice.

    3. Verify the camper's health record for a history of varicella. If negative, isolate the child and notify the oncologist.

    4. Administer 250 mg of acetylsalicylic acid (Aspirin) to the child and encourage him to rest.

103. Due to cancer therapy, some of the campers have bleeding tendencies. How should the nurse protect herself from bloodborne infections while caring for these children?

    1. Initiate universal precautions when in contact with campers' vomitus, urine, or sputum.

    2. Wear gloves if there is a risk of contact with campers' visibly bloody body fluids.

    3. Wear latex gloves when assisting campers with personal hygiene.

    4. Institute barrier precautions for campers with open wounds.

104. Christa and Brian, two 16-year-old campers who are receiving chemotherapy, have developed a close relationship during their time together at camp. Brian asks the nurse if she can give him some condoms. What is the most appropriate approach by the nurse?

    1. Explain to Brian that because he and Christa are immunocompromised they should not have sexual relations.

    2. Explain to Brian that parental consent is required before he can be provided with condoms.

    3. Delay responding to Brian's request until the matter can be discussed with Christa.

    4. Provide condoms to Brian, explain their use, and invite further discussion.

105. Cathy, a 12-year-old camper, has a tunnelled central venous catheter that requires a dressing change twice a week. She wishes to go on a 7-day canoe trip. What should the nurse do to promote the integrity of the catheter site?

    1. Tell Cathy to shorten the canoe trip to accommodate her scheduled dressing change.

    2. Ensure Cathy can demonstrate the skill of changing her own dressing.

    3. Teach Cathy's counsellor how to change the dressing.

    4. Change Cathy's dressing immediately prior to and following the trip.

End of case 23

Case 24

Lonnie, 6 years old, was diagnosed with asthma one year ago. His mother brings him to the clinic for a regular follow-up visit. She tells the nurse that Lonnie is taking metered doses of salbutamol (Ventolin) 2 puffs p.r.n., beclomethasone (Becloforte) 2 puffs b.i.d. During the interview, the nurse learns that Lonnie coughs frequently during the night, often feels winded during gym class, and has missed 10 days of school in the last 6 months. She also learns that Lonnie's mother smokes in the home, and that the family has a cat.

QUESTIONS 106 to 111 refer to this case.

106. When asked her overall opinion of Lonnie's health, his mother remarks that she thinks his health is good for a child with asthma. Considering the opinion that Lonnie's mother has expressed regarding Lonnie's state of health, which response by the nurse would be most appropriate?

    1. "Yes, Lonnie's asthma is as well controlled as we can hope."
    2. "Lonnie's health will not improve until you stop smoking."
    3. "I want to refer you to the doctor to review Lonnie's medications."
    4. "What have you been told about the level of control of asthma symptoms you can expect?"

107. Lonnie and his mother discuss with the nurse ways to manage Lonnie's asthma symptoms. Which strategy would best reduce his night coughing?

    1. Suggest that Lonnie's bedroom window be left open to increase fresh airflow.
    2. Inform Lonnie that the cat should be kept out of his room after bedtime.
    3. Teach Lonnie and his mother how to use a peak flow monitor to determine when Lonnie should use his Ventolin inhaler.
    4. Recommend to Lonnie's mother that she sign up for a smoking cessation program.

108. Lonnie indicates he rarely plays with the other children at recess because "he can't keep up." What activity would be most beneficial to him physically and socially?

    1. Playing in the sandbox.
    2. Joining in baseball games.
    3. Participating in soccer games.
    4. Playing a game on the computer.

109. Lonnie's mother is concerned that if Lonnie increases his activity level he will aggravate his asthma. Drawing on evidence-based nursing knowledge, what should the nurse respond to ease her concerns?

    1. "Mothers tell me that their children limit their own activity."
    2. "I rarely see children admitted to hospital with asthma because of excess activity."
    3. "The doctor will be able to recommend the best activity level for Lonnie."
    4. "Research shows that if Lonnie uses his Ventolin before exercise, he should not have any difficulty."

110. Lonnie says some of the children at school will not play with him because they are afraid they will catch asthma from him. Which approach to teaching Lonnie's schoolmates about asthma would be most effective for improving his peer relationships?

1. The nurse requests that Lonnie's teacher explain asthma to his schoolmates.
2. With help from Lonnie, the nurse teaches his schoolmates about asthma.
3. The nurse suggests to Lonnie's mother that she contact the mothers of his classmates, and ask them to tell their children about asthma.
4. The nurse develops and implements a teaching plan about asthma for Lonnie's schoolmates.

111. During the interview, Lonnie's mother mentions that he often complains of being treated like a baby by his family because of his asthma. Which of the following activities would be appropriate for the nurse to suggest to deal with Lonnie's complaint?

1. "You might talk to Lonnie about some chores he could help with, such as helping you prepare supper."
2. "If Lonnie is awake at night, you might let him stay and watch television."
3. "Arrange borrowing privileges at the library so Lonnie can borrow a children's book about asthma."
4. "You might encourage Lonnie to develop a hobby such as building model airplanes."

End of case 24

Case 25

The nurse from the public health unit has been requested by the program director at a seniors' complex to plan and establish a program for a group of men, ages 65 to 75 years. The nurse will address health problems for which this age group is at risk.

QUESTIONS 112 to 117 refer to this case.

112. While preparing for a session on prostate cancer, the nurse recognizes her own discomfort about discussing sexual issues with men in this age group. How should the nurse deal with her feelings?

1. Reflect on why nurses feel discomfort discussing sexuality issues.
2. Accept her own inability to openly discuss sexuality issues with this group.
3. Decide to refrain from discussing sexuality until her level of comfort improves.
4. Talk to a colleague about her feelings of discomfort in discussing sexual issues.

113. In view of the increased incidence of prostate cancer among older Canadian men, which of the following topics would be important for the nurse to include in her discussion?

1. Signs and symptoms of prostate cancer
2. Screening practices for prostate cancer
3. Treatments for prostate cancer
4. Rising mortality rates of prostate cancer

114. At the beginning of the educational session, which includes a video on prostate cancer, the nurse finds the group apprehensive and embarassed to discuss the topic. Considering the group's behaviour, how should the nurse approach this situation?

    1. Acknowledge the group's discomfort with the topic.
    2. Reduce the apprehension by telling an amusing anecdote.
    3. Recognize this is a common response in this age group and begin the session.
    4. Give the group time to ease into the topic by starting the session with the video.

115. During the session, one of the men makes a comment that his friend was treated for prostate cancer and now he can no longer have an erection. He wonders if this happens to everyone. How should the nurse respond to this comment?

    1. "Unfortunately, men who undergo surgery for prostate cancer are impotent, which is a good reason to prevent it."
    2. "Impotence is a common occurrence after prostate surgery, but there is no physiological reason why this occurs. With counselling it can be overcome."
    3. "I am glad you made that comment. No, not all men will have that experience."
    4. "That is a good question, which I encourage you to ask your doctor. Our focus is the prevention of prostate cancer, not treatment."

116. At the end of the session on prostate cancer, some men in the group are anxious to be screened as soon as possible. How can the nurse promote continuity of care?

    1. Contact a physician on behalf of the group to obtain an appointment for each man.
    2. Encourage the men to schedule appointments with their family physicians.
    3. Arrange to have a nurse practitioner come to the seniors' complex to hold a screening clinic.
    4. Offer to screen any of the men who are expressing concern about being screened.

117. Which statement by one of the group participants demonstrates understanding of the risk factors for prostate cancer?

    1. "Walking daily will reduce the risk of getting prostate cancer."
    2. "It is important to have the screening tests every year."
    3. "I know that frequent urination is a sign of prostate cancer."
    4. "From now on I plan to eat only organic produce."

End of case 25

4

Independent questions

QUESTIONS 118 to 130 do *not* refer to a case.

118. Which approach by the nurse is most likely to facilitate continuity and consistency of a client's care?

1. Co-ordinate regular client-focused conferences attended by relevant health team members.
2. Identify the client's health care needs on behalf of all health team members.
3. Communicate individually with each health team member.
4. Make decisions regarding the client's care based on input from all health team members.

119. A mother expresses reluctance to stay with her 2-year-old child while his IV is being started. Which response by the nurse is most helpful?

1. "If you would feel better waiting in the parent room, I can stay with her while the IV is being started."
2. "I understand that it is hard to see your child experiencing pain, but it will help her if you are there."
3. "I can see that this is upsetting you. Some parents just cannot bear to see their children in pain."
4. "It is frightening for a child to have an IV started. She will be less afraid if you stay with her."

120. When teaching a client recovering from a cerebral vascular accident to begin mobilizing with a cane, which instruction should the nurse give the client?

1. "Hold the cane with your weak hand."
2. "Move the cane and your strong leg together."
3. "Move forward with your weak leg first."
4. "Move the cane forward first."

121. Joseph, 4 years old, has daily physiotherapy for burns to his arms and chest. His mother says she cannot attend the physiotherapy sessions any more because they cause her son so much discomfort. Which response by the nurse would be most supportive?

1. "The physiotherapy does hurt but he really has to have it."
2. "You are welcome to stay in the parent room while he has the physiotherapy."
3. "Would you like me to ask the doctor to cut back on the amount of physiotherapy?"
4. "Could someone else in your family stay with him during physiotherapy so you could have a break?"

122. A client smelling of alcohol comes to the emergency room vomiting, speaking loudly, and staggering. His wife states that he has been drinking for a week. How should the nurse intervene?

1. Perform a physical assessment including Glasgow coma scale, and place him where he can be monitored.
2. Provide an emesis basin and place the client and his wife in a private room.
3. Assess his vital signs, administer oral fluids, and refer them to the community addiction centre.
4. Notify the emergency physician, accept a telephone order for dimenhydrinate (Gravol), and administer the medication rectally.

123. A nurse administers 40 units of Humulin R insulin to a client instead of 4 units. What actions should the nurse take?

    1. Inform the client of the error, give the client an oral concentrated glucose solution, advise the physician, and complete a medication error report.

    2. Give the client a glass of orange juice, observe for signs of hypoglycemia, and document actions taken in the client's record.

    3. Take a stat capillary glucose, observe for signs of hypoglycemia, hold the next dose of insulin, and advise the physician.

    4. Inform the client of the error, give the client a glass of orange juice, and observe for signs of hypoglycemia.

124. During the final practicum, a student nurse tells the supervising nurse that his client assignment is heavier than he can handle. The student requests that the nurse either change the assignment or assist him with the care. What is the supervising nurse's best response?

    1. "In the present practice environment, nurses have to manage a heavy client load."

    2. "If you can manage this morning, I will do some of your treatments this afternoon."

    3. "Let's talk about what specifically you feel is beyond your capabilities."

    4. "I will change your assignment so that you will not feel unsafe."

125. Sarah, 8 years old, is hospitalized with a serious illness. When the nurse comes by on her rounds, she finds Sarah being visited by her parents and her twin sister Anna. Hospital policy allows only 2 visitors per client. Which action demonstrates the nurse using proper professional judgment when following hospital policy?

    1. Inform Sarah's family that one of them must leave.

    2. Let Sarah know that her family can stay for a few more minutes, but must then say goodbye.

    3. Overlook this minor policy violation.

    4. Offer Sarah's family the option of staying after advising the charge nurse.

126. A 45-year-old client presents himself at a small rural hospital emergency room with shortness of breath and wheezing. Hospital policy permits the physician to order medications over the phone and send the client home without examining him. In this nurse's judgment, the physician should examine this client due to the acuity of his condition. The physician refuses to examine the client. What should be the nurse's next course of action?

    1. Tell the client to go to a neighbouring hospital where a physician is available.

    2. Accept the phone order and administer the medications.

    3. Call another physician for an opinion.

    4. Consult the charge nurse immediately.

127. A nurse, just prior to break time, completes a dressing change on a 10-year-old child. Which action by the nurse shows proper application of principles of documentation?

    1. Record the condition of the wound and care provided in the nurses' notes following the completion of the procedure.

    2. Report the condition of the wound to a colleague prior to taking a break.

    3. Document the completion of the dressing change in the nurses notes at the end of the shift.

    4. Record the condition of the wound and care provided in the nurse's notes following the break.

128. A nurse is faced with the following concurrent problems: a client who has vomited "all her supper," a client with chest pain, a client requesting medication for postoperative pain "that's getting bad again," and a ringing phone. Which should be the nurse's first and second priority?

1. Answer the phone, then attend to the client with chest pain.
2. Assess the client with chest pain, then administer medication to postoperative client.
3. Assist the client who has vomited, then attend to the client with chest pain.
4. Attend to the client with chest pain, then answer the phone.

129. Upon returning to the unit after a break, the nurse discovers that a client's IV has gone interstitial, another client is on the floor having fallen out of bed, and a third client requires a postoperative admission. What should the nurse do first?

1. Attend to the client who requires the postoperative admission.
2. Remove the interstitial IV from the client's arm.
3. Call for assistance from a colleague.
4. Assist the fallen client to a chair.

130. A nurse is in charge of an evening shift and is working with one registered nurse and one practical nurse. Half way through the shift, one of the practical nurse's clients becomes acutely ill and requires advanced interventions and close monitoring. What actions should the nurse take?

1. Inform the physician that the care of this client will overload the unit.
2. Ask the family to assist with the client's care and to report any changes.
3. Ask the practical care nurse to continue to care for the client but to report frequently on his status.
4. Call for a brief conference with her two colleagues and reassign the client to an RN.

End of independent questions

End of examination

Chapter 5
Scoring the practice exam

Scoring the Practice Exam

Calculating Your Score

The following steps can be used to calculate your total raw score on the Practice Exam.

1. Locate the answer key for the Practice Exam (see pages 96 and 97). Note that there is one key per exam book.

2. Tally up your responses that correspond to the correct answers indicated on the answer key. (Identify those questions you answered incorrectly by circling or highlighting them on your answer sheet, or by listing them on a separate sheet of paper. This will make it easier for you to create your Performance Profile, an exercise which is explained in the next chapter.)

3. Score one point for each correct answer. There is no penalty for incorrect or blank responses; they receive a score of zero. Be sure to scan your answer sheet for "double responses" to questions (i.e., where you selected more than one answer to a single question). Double responses are scored as zero, even if one of the answers selected is correct.

4. Use the chart below to record your score on each exam book and to calculate your total raw score.

Number of questions answered correctly
Book I . . . . ___/130
Book II . . . . ___/130
Total Raw Score (Sum of Books I + II) . . . . ___/260

5. Once you have added together your scores for each book in the Practice Exam, you will have your total raw score. The next calculation you can make is to convert your total raw score into a percentage score. This may be done using the following formula:

Percentage score
$\dfrac{\text{Total Raw Score}}{260} \times 100 = \underline{\quad}\%$

Interpreting Your Score

Although the total raw score and percentage score that you calculate are of a different type than the result you would receive on the actual RN Exam (see next section), they can provide useful feedback on your performance. By using the Score Interpretation Scale on page 95, you can obtain a quick assessment of your performance on the Practice Exam, along with some follow-up steps you should take to enhance your preparation for the RN Exam. Note that no specific pass mark is set for the Practice Exam.

5

How the Actual RN Exam is Scored

The RN Exam is computer scored by Assessment Strategies Inc. Only answers recorded on your answer sheets are scanned and scored. You will not receive any credit for questions that you only answered directly in the exam books and not on the answer sheets. Likewise, no credit will be given where you selected more than one answer to a single question. It is essential that you read and follow the instructions inside each exam book on how to correctly mark your selected answers; otherwise, your score may be adversely affected.

Once your answer sheets for both exam books are scanned, your score on the examination is calculated and your "pass" or "fail" result is determined by comparing this score to the established standard (or pass mark).

The standard to be met on the RN Exam is established, prior to the administration of the examination, using a criterion-referenced approach. Such an approach involves setting the standard in reference to the content and the difficulty of the test questions. This is in contrast to the norm-referenced approach, which sets the standard in relation to the performance of the candidates.

The standard-setting procedure used involves convening panels of subject matter experts from across Canada to determine a point on a measurement scale that represents the expected performance of a minimally competent nurse beginning to practise. These subject matter experts are nurses who work closely with nurses beginning to practise, and include educators, experienced practitioners, and administrators. Prior to performing their task, the subject matter experts are provided with an extensive orientation and training by Assessment Strategies Inc. staff, to ensure that they produce ratings based on the same understanding of the minimally competent nurse beginning to practise.

In addition to the expert ratings, a variety of relevant data is carefully considered to ensure that the standard candidates will be required to achieve on the exam is valid and fair. This can include information on the preparation of new graduates, data on the performance of candidates on previously administered exams, and pertinent psychometric research findings. Based on all of this information, a point is set on a measurement scale that represents the minimum acceptable standard.

Regardless of the version of the examination that is administered, a candidate's score is converted to a common measurement scale and compared against the established passing point on that scale. Although different forms of the exam contain different sets of questions, this conversion ensures that all candidates are treated fairly and are evaluated against the same standard. If your score on this common scale is at or higher than the passing point, you will receive a "pass" result on the exam and if your score is lower than the passing point you will receive a "fail" result on the exam.

Your pass/fail result on the RN Exam is reported on an *Examination Performance Profile for Candidates* that is sent to you by your regulatory authority. Candidates who fail the RN Exam are also provided with feedback on their test performance. This feedback is similar to the information you will obtain by creating your Performance Profile (see Chapter 6).

Score Interpretation Scale

Raw Score	Practice Exam Performance	Suggestions for Follow-up
230	**STRONG**	Review the rationales of those questions you answered incorrectly. The closer your score is to the borderline zone, the more you should consult the relevant texts that are referenced. As well, by creating your Performance Profile (see Chapter 6), you may identify specific areas on which you should focus during your remaining preparation time. Before writing the RN Exam, take another look at the Practice Exam questions that you answered incorrectly.
210		
200		
190	**BORDERLINE**	Create your Performance Profile to determine your areas of strength and weakness, and follow the strategies provided for dealing with your identified weaknesses (see Chapter 6). Be sure to review some general nursing textbooks, concentrating on the problematic areas, and consult specific textbooks to increase your knowledge before taking the RN Exam. Following your review, retake the Practice Exam.
180		
170		
110		Create your Performance Profile (see Chapter 6) to gain a better understanding of your areas of weakness in the four (4) categories. In addition to reviewing some key nursing textbooks, be sure to read the rationales for all the questions in the Practice Exam. You may also benefit from reviewing the test-taking strategies in Chapter 3. Finally, retake the Practice Exam before taking the actual RN Exam.
90	**WEAK**	

5

Answer Key for Prep Guide Exam – Book 1

Question Number	Correct Answer	Question Number	Correct Answer	Question Number	Correct Answer	Question Number	Correct Answer
1.	4	34.	3	67.	1	100.	1
2.	1	35.	3	68.	1	101.	3
3.	2	36.	3	69.	2	102.	2
4.	4	37.	4	70.	2	103.	3
5.	3	38.	3	71.	3	104.	3
6.	1	39.	3	72.	2	105.	3
7.	3	40.	3	73.	2	106.	1
8.	2	41.	4	74.	3	107.	3
9.	3	42.	4	75.	1	108.	2
10.	1	43.	3	76.	1	109.	2
11.	2	44.	4	77.	3	110.	2
12.	1	45.	2	78.	2	111.	3
13.	2	46.	1	79.	2	112.	2
14.	1	47.	1	80.	2	113.	4
15.	4	48.	1	81.	1	114.	3
16.	1	49.	1	82.	4	115.	4
17.	2	50.	1	83.	2	116.	4
18.	4	51.	2	84.	4	117.	3
19.	1	52.	3	85.	4	118.	4
20.	2	53.	2	86.	3	119.	2
21.	4	54.	4	87.	4	120.	2
22.	2	55.	3	88.	3	121.	2
23.	3	56.	2	89.	2	122.	3
24.	3	57.	4	90.	1	123.	4
25.	1	58.	3	91.	2	124.	4
26.	2	59.	3	92.	2	125.	4
27.	1	60.	2	93.	4	126.	1
28.	1	61.	4	94.	2	127.	4
29.	1	62.	1	95.	3	128.	3
30.	4	63.	1	96.	2	129.	2
31.	1	64.	3	97.	2	130.	2
32.	3	65.	2	98.	2		
33.	4	66.	2	99.	2		

Answer Key for Prep Guide Exam – Book 2

Question Number	Correct Answer
1.	2
2.	3
3.	1
4.	3
5.	3
6.	3
7.	2
8.	2
9.	3
10.	4
11.	3
12.	4
13.	3
14.	4
15.	4
16.	4
17.	1
18.	4
19.	2
20.	4
21.	3
22.	2
23.	2
24.	4
25.	2
26.	3
27.	2
28.	1
29.	3
30.	2
31.	2
32.	2
33.	3

Question Number	Correct Answer
34.	1
35.	3
36.	2
37.	2
38.	3
39.	1
40.	2
41.	3
42.	2
43.	3
44.	3
45.	2
46.	3
47.	4
48.	1
49.	4
50.	4
51.	3
52.	3
53.	1
54.	3
55.	4
56.	4
57.	3
58.	4
59.	4
60.	4
61.	2
62.	2
63.	3
64.	3
65.	4
66.	3

Question Number	Correct Answer
67.	3
68.	2
69.	1
70.	1
71.	3
72.	3
73.	2
74.	3
75.	3
76.	3
77.	1
78.	3
79.	3
80.	1
81.	3
82.	4
83.	2
84.	4
85.	4
86.	3
87.	4
88.	1
89.	1
90.	4
91.	4
92.	4
93.	2
94.	4
95.	2
96.	3
97.	2
98.	2
99.	4

Question Number	Correct Answer
100.	2
101.	2
102.	3
103.	2
104.	4
105.	2
106.	4
107.	3
108.	2
109.	4
110.	2
111.	1
112.	4
113.	2
114.	1
115.	3
116.	2
117.	2
118.	1
119.	1
120.	4
121.	4
122.	1
123.	1
124.	3
125.	4
126.	4
127.	1
128.	2
129.	3
130.	4

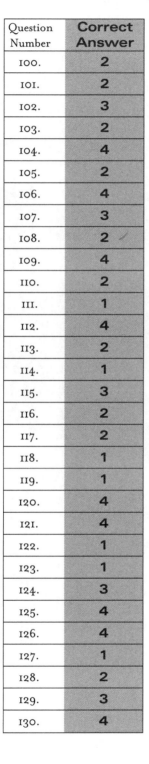

5

Chapter 6
Creating your performance profile

Creating Your Performance Profile

Once you have completed and scored the Practice Exam, it is possible to create a personalized Performance Profile that allows you to identify your areas of strength and weakness on the exam, based on the competency categories, the taxonomic levels, client types and age groups. You will need your scored answer sheets (or a list of the questions you answered incorrectly), the Performance Profile Tally Sheet and Performance Profile Chart (found in the Additional Materials at the end of the *Prep Guide*), and a calculator.

Classification of Questions

Each question in the Practice Exam has been classified within four different classification schemes: Competency Category, Taxonomic Level, Client Type and Age Group. Each question's classifications are indicated beside the question's rationale in Chapter 7.

All these classification schemes are weighted elements from the *Blueprint*, and an explanation of these can be found in Chapter 2.

Steps for Creating Your Performance Profile

1. In scoring your Practice Exam with the information provided in the previous chapter, you identified on your answer sheets (or on a separate sheet), those questions you answered incorrectly. For each question answered **incorrectly** place an X beside the corresponding classifications in the rationale section (Chapter 7).

2. The **Performance Profile Tally Sheet** and the **Performance Profile Chart** are located at the back of the Prep Guide and can be easily removed for you to use. Each of these contain four tables. In Table 1 of the Tally Sheet, for each question you answered incorrectly, place a mark in the row that corresponds to the Competency Category for that question (see Sample – Step 2). Similarly, in Table 2, place a mark in the row that corresponds to the taxonomic level for each question you answered **incorrectly**. The same can be done for the Client Type table and the Age Group table.

SAMPLE – STEP 2
PERFORMANCE PROFILE TALLY SHEET

Table 1: Competency Category

CATEGORY		TOTAL INCORRECT		% INCORRECT
N-CR	~~HHT~~ /		÷ 21 X 100 =	%
HP	~~HHT~~ ~~HHT~~		÷ 42 X 100 =	%
I/IP	~~HHT~~ ////		÷ 28 X 100 =	%
C/SC	~~HHT~~ ~~HHT~~ ~~HHT~~ ~~HHT~~ ~~HHT~~ ~~HHT~~		÷ 112 X 100 =	
RC	~~HHT~~ //			
PP				

6

3. Next, total the rows in each table to determine the number of questions you answered incorrectly in each category.

4. Then, calculate the percentage of questions you answered incorrectly for each category. To calculate the percentage, divide the number of questions you answered incorrectly by the total number of questions for that category (found at the end of the row) and multiply by 100 (see Sample – Step 3 and 4).

SAMPLE – STEPS 3 and 4
PERFORMANCE PROFILE TALLY SHEET

Table 1: Competency Category

CATEGORY		TOTAL INCORRECT			% INCORRECT
N–CR	~~HHT~~ /	6	÷ 21	X 100 =	29 %
HP	~~HHT~~ ~~HHT~~	10	÷ 42	X 100 =	24 %
I/IP	~~HHT~~ ////	9	÷ 28	X 100 =	32 %
C/SC	~~HHT~~ ~~HHT~~ ~~HHT~~ ~~HHT~~ ~~HHT~~ ~~HHT~~	30	÷ 112	X 100 =	
RC	~~HHT~~ //				

5. Your performance profile can now be created by taking the percentage values from each category and darkening the corresponding rows on the Performance Profile Chart (see Sample – Step 5).

SAMPLE – STEP 5
PERFORMANCE PROFILE CHART

Table 1: Competency Category

% OF INCORRECT ANSWERS

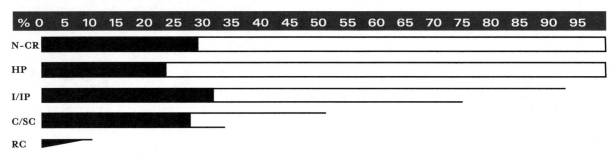

Interpretation of Performance

The goal in creating your Performance Profile is to identify your areas of relative strength and weakness. This information can help you in making the best use of your remaining preparation time.

Competency Category Results

Generally, those categories in which you selected a high percentage of incorrect answers are the areas you should focus on during your remaining preparation time. However, this approach can be refined somewhat to arrive at a more accurate diagnosis.

In looking at each table on the tally sheets, you will notice that the number of questions in each category varies (i.e., the number by which you must divide); some areas have relatively few questions whereas other have many. This is an important aspect in understanding your performance. Both the percentage of incorrect responses in a category and the total number of incorrect responses in a category should be carefully considered to make a complete interpretation of your performance.

You will recall that the Competency Category is a weighted element of the examination *Blueprint*. This means that the number of questions on the exam from each competency category is set and that this number is not equal for each category. The distribution of questions on the Practice Exam, by category, is as follows:

— Nurse-Client Relationship: 9%
— Health Promotion: 16%
— Illness/Injury Prevention: 11%
— Curative/Supportive Care: 40%
— Rehabilitative Care: 9%
— Professional Practice: 16%

The following example will help to illustrate the importance of considering both the percentage and the number of incorrect responses in a category. If your profile chart shows that you selected the highest percentage of incorrect answers in the Rehabilitative Care category in Table 1, you should keep in mind that a relatively small number of questions on the exam deal with Rehabilitative Care (i.e., approximately 21 questions out of the total of 260). Even if you selected only correct responses for that category, the impact on your total score would be relatively small. On the other hand, a fairly small percentage of incorrect responses in the Curative/Supportive Care category (with as many as 104 questions out of the total 260) can represent many questions on the exam. Consequently, improving your performance in this category by only a few percentage marks can make a greater difference overall.

Therefore, although a high percentage of incorrect responses in a competency category is certainly an indication of a weakness in that category, your best strategy for studying may require you to focus in an other category, one that has a greater representation on the exam.

Once you have determined which competency categories you need to improve in, you may wish to follow the three steps below:

1. Go to Appendix A and review the competencies in the categories identified as areas of weakness for you; this will give you an overview of the competencies that require your attention.

2. Review the questions that are classified in the competency categories you have identified as weaker for you. Include in your review both the questions you answered correctly as well as those you answered incorrectly; this will give a more complete review of the content that measures the competencies you need to improve on. Be sure to read the rationales for the correct and incorrect responses to get a better understanding of your areas of weakness.

6

3. Look up the references cited (or other comparable references) for the questions you answered incorrectly; this can increase your understanding of material you may not have yet fully mastered.

Taxonomic Level, Client Type, and Age Group

The interpretation approach given for the competency categories also applies to your results in the other three categories because they too represent a weighted element of the *Blueprint*.

As a strategy for dealing with your identified area(s) of weakness in these areas, you may wish to follow the three steps below:

1. Verify your understanding of the categories that are causing difficulties for you. This can be done by reviewing the definition of these categories which are provided in Chapter 2. You should also note the relative weight of each category.

2. Review all the questions that have been classified in your weaker categories. Include the questions that you answered correctly as well as those you answered incorrectly. This will provide for a more complete review of the categories in question.

3. Look up the references cited (or other comparable references) to review the more detailed information they will offer on the content with which you had difficulty.

Finally, you can retake the Practice Exam after having completed your review and preparation. By following the suggested strategies for dealing with your results, you should see an improvement in your overall score as well as in your Performance Profile results.

Chapter 7
Rationales for practice
exam questions

Book 1
Rationales

1. correct answer: 4

1. At some point in time such a visit would be helpful but is not needed immediately upon admission.

2. This is a standard nursing intervention for women with pre-eclampsia and would be implemented upon hospital admission. However, it would not assist the parents with their immediate concerns.

3. This is leading the parents into making a decision that may not be feasible. The nurse does not have sufficient information to make such a suggestion.

4. **The parents have identified child care as their immediate concern. This would assist the parents to access child care services. Responding to their priorities may facilitate compliance with care goals.**

Classification

Competency Category:	Nurse-Client Relationship
Taxonomic Level:	Critical Thinking
Client Type:	Families
Age Group:	Adult

References

Pillitteri, A. (1999), pp. 396-397.

Lowdermilk, D. L., Perry, S. E., & Bobak, I. M. (1999), pp. 652-655.

2. correct answer: 1

1. **Provides consistent blood pressure information and baseline data for trending.**

2. If electronic devices are used, a manual reading should be done to validate the electronic device. Discrepancies have been shown between the two methods.

3. In fact, it is important to measure both the sitting and lying blood pressures in pre-eclampsia in order to assess positional adaptation abilities.

4. Activity and emotional distress can affect blood pressure readings.

Classification

Competency Category:	Curative/Supportive Care
Taxonomic Level:	Knowledge/Comprehension
Client Type:	Individuals
Age Group:	Adult

References

Pillitteri, A. (1999), pp. 396-397.

Lowdermilk, D. L., Perry, S. E., & Bobak, I. M. (1999), pp. 645-646.

3. correct answer: 2

1. Such a collection would be appropriate for an assessment of intact fetoplacental unit but is not the priority intervention.

2. **This is important in order to assess for the potential of antepartum hemorrhage due to the blunt trauma to the abdomen.**

3. This is contraindicated if placental injury is suspected.

4. This is inappropriate, as internal fetal monitoring cannot be done unless the membranes have ruptured.

Classification

Competency Category:	Curative/Supportive Care
Taxonomic Level:	Critical Thinking
Client Type:	Individuals
Age Group:	Adult

References

Pillitteri, A. (1999), p. 385.

Lowdermilk, D. L., Perry, S. E., & Bobak, I. M. (1999), pp. 674-678.

4. correct answer: 4

1. This is more applicable to the hypertension diagnosis.

2. The client is not indicating the presence of pain or respiratory difficulty.

3. More applicable to cardiac dysfunction situations.

4. **The client's fetus is at an increased risk for intrauterine compromise due to premature separation of the placenta.**

Classification

Competency Category:	Curative/Supportive Care
Taxonomic Level:	Application
Client Type:	Individuals
Age Group:	Adult

References

Pillitteri, A. (1999), pp. 396-398.

Lowdermilk, D. L., Perry, S. E., & Bobak, I. M. (1999), p. 676.

5. correct answer: 3

1. At some point this would be helpful. However, the family wants more immediate action, not necessarily discussion.

2. This may also be necessary if discussion with the resident is unsuccessful. This would not be appropriate at this time without first trying to resolve the problem with the resident.

3. **It is not appropriate to go over a professional's decision without first discussing it with her or him. Contacting the attending physician is necessary if the inital communication is unsatisfactory or non-responsive. Contacting the attending physician is within the standards of practice for accountability and advocacy.**

4. To advocate is to act on behalf of a client in order to provide high quality care. Suggesting that the client's husband communicate with the attending physician himself is not advocating for the client.

Classification

Competency Category:	Professional Practice
Taxonomic Level:	Application
Client Type:	Families
Age Group:	Adult

References

Arnold, E., & Boggs, K. U. (1995), pp. 514, 516.

Taylor, C., Lillis, C., & LeMone, P. (1997), pp. 424-426.

6. correct answer: 1

1. **The nurse provides a choice to the parents. This intervention will allow the parents to hold their child and say goodbye.**

2. This option does not give a choice to the parents and may not be acceptable to them.

3. This is an inappropriate reassurance as it downplays the significance of the current pregnancy and loss.

4. The parents may want the support of extended family at this time. The restriction of visitors would not help them during their grieving.

Classification

Competency Category:	Curative/Supportive Care
Taxonomic Level:	Application
Client Type:	Families
Age Group:	Adult

References

Pillitteri, A. (1999), pp. 406-407.

Lowdermilk, D. L., Perry, S. E., & Bobak, I. M. (1999), pp. 735-738.

7

7. correct answer: 3

1. Overtreatment for hypoglycemia with quick-acting carbohydrates such as a candy bar should be avoided.

2. High-fat foods and high-protein foods should not be used to initially correct hypoglycemia.

3. **At the first sign of hypoglycemia, the client should ingest a simple fast-acting carbohydrate such as orange juice.**

4. Clients are encouraged to refrain from eating high-calorie, high-fat dessert food such as cookies, cakes and ice-cream, to treat hypoglycemia.

Classification

Competency Category:	Health Promotion
Taxonomic Level:	Application
Client Type:	Individuals
Age Group:	Adult

References

Lewis, S. M., Collier, I. C., & Heitkemper, M. M. (1996), pp. 1468-1469.
Smeltzer, S. C., & Bare, B. G. (1996), pp. 1046-1047.

8. correct answer: 2

1. The client is worsening and a more appropriate intervention is needed. She is also at risk of choking if she eats because she is stuporous.

2. **Glucagon 1 mg, IM can be administered for fast action. It stimulates a strong response to convert glycogen to glucose making the glucose readily available. Response is seen in 5-20 minutes.**

3. D5W does not contain sufficient glucose to raise the client's blood sugar.

4. Time is of the essence as the client's condition may deteriorate even faster and become critical.

Classification

Competency Category:	Curative/Supportive Care
Taxonomic Level:	Critical Thinking
Client Type:	Individuals
Age Group:	Adult

References

Lewis, S. M., Collier, I. C., & Heitkemper, M. M. (1996), pp. 1468-1469.
Smeltzer, S. C., & Bare, B. G. (1996), pp. 1048-1049.

9. correct answer: 3

1. Equals only 1,000 mg per day.
2. Equals 1,500 mg per day.
3. **500 mg x 4 times daily = 2,000 mg or 2 g gives correct daily dose.**
4. Equals 3,000 mg per day.

Classification

Competency Category:	Curative/Supportive Care
Taxonomic Level:	Application
Client Type:	Individuals
Age Group:	Adult

References

Elkin, M. K., Perry, A. G., & Potter, P. A. (1996), pp. 290-293.
Potter, P. A., & Perry, A. G. (1995), pp. 655-657.
Taylor, C., Lillis, C., & LeMone, P. (1997), p. 607.

10. correct answer: 1

1. **Regular insulin is used for emergencies. This step-order process avoids the problem of contaminating the regular insulin vial with intermediate insulin. Regular insulin will bind with NPH in the vial which reduces the action of the regular insulin.**
2. Shaking causes bubbles to form which are aspirated in the syringe, take up space and alter the dosage.
3. This step-order process contaminates regular insulin with intermediate insulin.
4. There is no need to aspirate in subcutaneous tissue, and this is an extra step she does not need to do. Vigorous massage of insulin is contraindicated as it speeds up the absorption time of insulin.

Classification

Competency Category:	Curative/Supportive Care
Taxonomic Level:	Application
Client Type:	Individuals
Age Group:	Adult

References

Elkin, M. K., Perry, A. G., & Potter, P. A. (1996), pp. 324-325.
Smeltzer, S. C., & Bare, B. G. (1996), pp. 1096-1099.

7

11. correct answer: 2

1. A program of balanced planned exercise is beneficial for the client with diabetes. She should not stop exercising or socializing with her friends.

2. **A potential risk for clients with diabetes is post-exercise hypoglycemia. They need to eat a protein and carbohydrate snack before exercising.**

3. Clients with diabetes should test their blood sugar before exercising. However, activity will lower the blood sugar and exercise is not contraindicated in the event the blood sugar is elevated.

4. To prevent a hypoglycemic reaction, the client should have a planned snack prior to exercise rather than wait for hypoglycemic reactions to occur. In the event of a hypoglycemic reaction, exercise should be stopped.

Classification

Competency Category:	Illness/Injury Prevention
Taxonomic Level:	Application
Client Type:	Individuals
Age Group:	Adult

References

Smeltzer, S. C., & Bare, B. G. (1996), pp. 1026-1027.

Phipps, W., Cassmeyer, V., Sands, J., & Lehman, M. (1995), pp. 1306-1310.

12. correct answer: 1

1. **A balanced food selection will ensure an adequate intake of necessary nutrients. To help control blood glucose levels, a diabetic meal should focus on control of total calorie intake to attain reasonable weight and control blood glucose.**

2. Fat content should be less than 30% of the total calories and this may help the reduction of the cholesterol level which is associated with coronary artery disease. Clients with diabetes are at risk for coronary artery disease.

3. Canada's Food Guide recommendations for food group servings is insufficient to control caloric intake.

4. A balanced diet should include less than 30% fat and 55% carbohydrates. An intake of fats equal to carbohydrates would increase the risk of coronary artery disease.

Classification

Competency Category:	Health Promotion
Taxonomic Level:	Application
Client Type:	Individuals
Age Group:	Adult

References

Lewis, S. M., Collier, I. C., & Heitkemper, M. M. (1996), pp. 1446-1447.

Smeltzer, S. C., & Bare, B. G. (1996), pp. 1024-1025.

13. correct answer: 2

1. It is essential that the nurse gather as much data on the client's medical history so that appropriate diagnostic and treatment measures can be initiated. This question is not relevant unless the roommate states that he hasn't known the client for long.

2. **A broad opening using an open-ended, unbiased question allows the roommate to consider and share with the nurse all areas of the client's health status and lifestyle. This approach would also save time as opposed to asking specific questions about several different areas.**

3. While this is an important question, the priority right now is to find the cause of the client's unconsciousness.

4. Although this information is important to know, this is a closed question that would elicit a yes or no answer. The information obtained from this question would likely be elicited by the reponse to the question in #2.

Classification

Competency Category:	Curative/Supportive Care
Taxonomic Level:	Critical Thinking
Client Type:	Individuals
Age Group:	Adult

References

Riley, J. W. (1996), pp. 163-164.
Stuart, G. W., & Laraia, M. T. (1998), p. 31.

7

14. correct answer: 1

1. **Respiratory arrest is a potential complication of overdoses of central nervous system depressants, such as alcohol and lorazepam. Cardiac arrhythmias are common side effects of cocaine abuse.**

2. Seizures can be a symptom of stimulant abuse, such as cocaine and amphetamines. Flashbacks are associated with prolonged use of hallucinogens, such as LSD.

3. Toxic psychosis is associated with marijuana abuse and overdose. Coronary artery vasoconstriction results from cocaine abuse leading to cardiac arrhythmias.

4. Delirium tremens or major alcohol withdrawal syndrome occur after sudden cessation of significant alcohol abuse over a period of 10 or more years. Hyperthermia is a serious and potentially fatal side effect of ingesting "Angel Dust," also known as Phencyclidine (PCP).

Classification

Competency Category: Curative/Supportive Care
Taxonomic Level: Application
Client Type: Individuals
Age Group: Adult

References

Boyd, M. A., & Nihart, M. A. (1998), pp. 720-721.

Stuart, G. W., & Laraia, M. T. (1998), pp. 492-493.

15. correct answer: 4

1. Unconscious clients should be positioned flat and on their sides to maintain a patent airway. Assessing for injuries would be a priority.

2. Blood glucose readings would not be relevant in this case. A condom catheter could be applied to keep the client dry and to monitor output in terms of his fluid balance status. Keeping an unconscious client warm is appropriate but these last two interventions are not a priority at this time.

3. Notifying client's parents is a priority but secondary to his physcial needs. Monitoring his respiratory status and level of consciousness q 1h would not be frequent enough when there is potential for respiratory arrest and cardiac arrhythmias.

4. **All of these interventions are a priority for clients with substance induced coma. Q 15 minute assessments facilitate early intervention.**

Classification

Competency Category:	Curative/Supportive Care
Taxonomic Level:	Application
Client Type:	Individuals
Age Group:	Adult

References

Phipps, W., Cassmeyer, V., Sands, J., & Lehman, M. (1995), p. 739.

Boyd, M. A., & Nihart, M. A. (1998), p. 1108.

16. correct answer: 1

1. **Denial is the biggest barrier to successfully treating individuals with substance abuse. Assuming responsibility for his substance abusing behaviour is key to successful treatment.**

2. Although peer support groups are the primary mode of treatment as they offer honest, supportive but confrontational sessions, the client should not only consider but make a commitment to join a support group.

3. Blaming others or circumstances gives the client an excuse to continue to abuse drugs and alcohol to deal with stress.

4. This is not a realistic discharge goal and may not be answerable. The unconscious reasons for substance abuse would require long-term psychotherapy.

Classification

Competency Category:	Curative/Supportive Care
Taxonomic Level:	Critical Thinking
Client Type:	Individuals
Age Group:	Adult

References

Haber, J., Krainovich-Miller, B., McMahon, A. L., & Price-Hoskins, P. (1997), pp. 527-535.

Schultz, J. M., & Videbeck, S. D. (1998), pp. 272-274.

7

17. correct answer: 2

1. This is an unnecessary step. The community health nurse would also refer the client to the appropriate community resource.

2. **This is an appropriate referral and the client will need assistance from the nurse in locating such a group. This would be one of the primary methods of support and treatment for him.**

3. This is a support group for partners of alcoholics.

4. This is a program for individuals addicted to heroin. This is not relevant for this client.

Classification

Competency Category:	Rehabilitative Care
Taxonomic Level:	Application
Client Type:	Individuals
Age Group:	Adult

References

Haber, J., Krainovich-Miller, B., McMahon, A. L., & Price-Hoskins, P. (1997), p. 534.

Miller, C. A. (1999), p. 635.

18. correct answer: 4

1. The primary nurse has a professional responsibility to intervene in this situation based on standards of practice.

2. It is an inappropriate step at this time for the primary nurse to report her colleague. She should first discuss this matter with the colleague in order to clarify the situation and allow the colleague to correct her behaviour.

3. It is more appropriate to discuss the matter with her colleague and allow the colleague to rectify the situation. It is inappropriate for the nurse to tell the client what he should or should not do.

4. **It is appropriate for the primary nurse to point out to her colleague that her behaviour is unprofessional and violates therapeutic boundaries. Establishing a social relationship with a client is a violation of therapeutic boundaries whether it occurs while the client is in hospital or after discharge. Attraction is a common positive countertransference reaction. Nurses should be aware of such reactions and not act on these feelings.**

Classification

Competency Category:	Professional Practice
Taxonomic Level:	Affective
Client Type:	Individuals
Age Group:	Adult

References

Haber, J., Krainovich-Miller, B., McMahon, A. L., & Price-Hoskins, P. (1997), pp. 154-157.

Stuart, G. W., & Laraia, M. T. (1998), pp. 48-50.

19. correct answer: 1

1. **The primary source of information is the client.**

2. The primary source of information is the client. Secondary resources include client's support persons/family.

3. The nursing assessment cannot be complete without information obtained from the client who is the primary source of information. Past health records are an informative but secondary source of assessment data.

4. The client is the primary source of information. However, to obtain a complete data base, the nurse must refer to other sources of information as well, which are termed secondary sources, such as the ambulance attendant.

Classification

Competency Category:	Curative/Supportive Care
Taxonomic Level:	Knowledge/Comprehension
Client Type:	Individuals
Age Group:	Adult

References

Taylor, C., Lillis, C., & LeMone, P. (1997), pp. 248-249.
DuGas, B. W., & Knor, E. R. (1995), pp. 334-335.

20. correct answer: 2

1. This will not answer the question asked by the client's wife. It just shows that the nurse is following doctor's orders.

2. **This will help the client and his wife understand that there is a relationship between the oxygen and the chest pain. Oxygen brings balance between myocardial supply and demand. Chest pain is one of the symptoms of ischemia/injury to the heart muscle.**

3. Oxygen is a standard of care in the treatment of myocardial ischemia and infarction. This explanation will not help the client and his wife understand the relationship between the treatment and the outcome.

4. The client's wife has asked the nurse for a response to her question. She may not gain confidence in the caregiver if the caregiver does not answer the question. Although the nurse will inform the physician, she should also respond to the question asked by the client's wife.

Classification

Competency Category:	Curative/Supportive Care
Taxonomic Level:	Application
Client Type:	Individuals
Age Group:	Adult

References

Smeltzer, S. C., & Bare, B. G. (1996), pp. 654-657.
Phipps, W., Cassmeyer, V., Sands, J., & Lehman, M. (1995), pp. 827-828.

7

21. correct answer: 4

1. Metoprolol is a beta blocker that will reduce the workload of the heart by reducing heart rate and blood pressure. It will not have an immediate effect. It is a scheduled medication, not p.r.n. The other interventions are appropriate.

2. Ativan will help relieve anxiety. However, the anxiety is most probably a result of the chest pain. The first and foremost intervention should be directed at relieving the pain and preventing injury to the myocardium.

3. Nitroglycerin is a vasodilator and will have an effect on blood pressure. If the blood pressure is too low, coronary artery perfusion will be further decreased, worsening the ischemia. The limit for sublingual nitroglycerin is 3 doses. Unrelieved pain indicates infarction.

4. **These interventions are all necessary, beneficial, appropriate, and safe.**

Classification

Competency Category:	Curative/Supportive Care
Taxonomic Level:	Critical Thinking
Client Type:	Individuals
Age Group:	Adult

References

Nettina, S. M. (1996), p. 290.

Smeltzer, S. C., & Bare, B. G. (1996), p. 650.

22. correct answer: 2

1. Morphine will reduce dyspnea and anxiety, reduce pulmonary capillary pressure and decrease seepage of fluid into the alveoli. It will decrease the respiratory rate but this is not a desired effect.

2. Morphine sulfate causes vasolidation and pooling of blood in peripheral blood vessels. Lasix causes diuresis which would decrease lung congestion. The combined effects of these medications produce the desired outcomes of improved oxygenation and decreased lung congestion.

3. These are not the desired effects of the medications. The pulse rate may go up or down depending on the circulatory volume status of the client and the level of anxiety. The respiratory rate may decrease as a result of the respiratory depression or improvement of dyspnea or reduction in anxiety.

4. These are side effects of the medications. The blood pressure may not change or may increase or decrease depending on the circulatory volume status of the client and the level of anxiety.

Classification

Competency Category:	Curative/Supportive Care
Taxonomic Level:	Application
Client Type:	Individuals
Age Group:	Adult

References

Nettina, S. M. (1996), p. 314.

Smeltzer, S. C., & Bare, B. G. (1996), p. 660.

7

23. correct answer: 3

1. This will interrupt the client's sleep cycle and is not therapeutic.

2. Delaying taking vital signs until the client wakes up, for an unknown period, may be unsafe. Vital signs should be taken within a specific time period to balance rest needs with assessment requirements. Mrs. Jacobs may inadvertently wake her husband up just so that he can be assessed.

3. The client's condition has stabilized. Sleep is essential to physical and mental well-being. 90 minutes allows for REM cycle to occur, which is essential for mental restoration. The nursing plan of care must provide for such periods of uninterrupted rest, and the necessity of taking vital signs every 1-2 hours must be weighed against the damage caused by sleep deprivation.

4. This will interrupt the client's sleep cycle. Sedative use is not indicated at this time.

Classification

Competency Category:	Health Promotion
Taxonomic Level:	Application
Client Type:	Individuals
Age Group:	Adult

References

Hudak, C. M., Gallo, B. M., & Morton, P. G. (1998), pp. 34-38.
Carpentino, L. J. (1997), pp. 836-837.

24. correct answer: 3

1. The nurse is not addressing the client's concerns regarding his diet.

2. The nurse is not demonstrating knowledge in the subject; this needs to be a permanent lifestyle change.

3. Effective client teaching requires that nurses have an adequate knowledge base supported by data from current research studies about risk factors and client compliance. The nurse also clarifies misconceptions the client may have about his diet.

4. It is important to assist the client in setting realistic goals for modifying the risk factors. Clients need to accept responsiblility for their health. It is not appropriate for the nurse to place responsibility on the wife to change her husband's habits.

Classification

Competency Category:	Illness/Injury Prevention
Taxonomic Level:	Application
Client Type:	Families
Age Group:	Adult

References

Smeltzer, S. C., & Bare, B. G. (1996), pp. 597, 639-640.
DuGas, B. W., & Knor, E. R. (1995), p. 144.

25. correct answer: 1

1. Facilitates the drainage of secretions and prevents the tongue from falling into the posterior pharynx and obstructing the airway.
2. Until the client is turned on his side and his respiratory status has been reassessed, there is not sufficient evidence that he needs an oral airway.
3. Providing care while the client remains on his back can cause him to aspirate.
4. Repositioning the client on his side should be done first. Mouth care is an inappropriate intervention as it does not clear the airway of secretions.

Classification

Competency Category:	Curative/Supportive Care
Taxonomic Level:	Application
Client Type:	Individuals
Age Group:	Adult

References

Eisenhauer, L. A., Nichols, L. W., & Bergon, F. W. (1998), p. 687.
Taylor, C., Lillis, C., & LeMone, P. (1997), p. 1062.

26. correct answer: 2

1. Incorrect calculation.
2. The correct calculation is:
   600 ml ÷ 75 ml per hour = 8 hours
   08 00 hours + 8 hours = 16 00 hours.
3. Incorrect calculation.
4. Incorrect calculation.

Classification

Competency Category:	Curative/Supportive Care
Taxonomic Level:	Knowledge/Comprehension
Client Type:	Individuals
Age Group:	Adult

References

Taylor, C., Lillis, C., & LeMone, P. (1997), p. 1423.
Craven, R. F., & Hirnle, C. (1996), p. 553.

7

27. correct answer: 1

1. The nurse should place the client's food and utensils on his unaffected side. Soft foods are indicated in cases of hemiparesis because of difficulty with chewing and swallowing.

2. The client cannot move his left side.

3. This does not encourage the client to feed himself. In addition, social interaction should be limited during mealtimes until the client can achieve adequate chewing and swallowing.

4. Social interaction should be limited during mealtimes until the client can achieve adequate chewing and swallowing.

Classification

Competency Category:	Rehabilitative Care
Taxonomic Level:	Application
Client Type:	Individuals
Age Group:	Adult

References

Thelan, L. A., Urden, L. D., Lough, M. E., & Stacy, K. M. (1998), p. 809.

Taylor, C., Lillis, C., & LeMone, P. (1997), p. 1064.

28. correct answer: 1

1. This explores the client's existing resources to determine if and what type of assistance the client's wife will require.

2. This is a costly suggestion and assumes this family has the necessary financial resources. In addition, a helper may not be required.

3. The client's existing resources should be determined prior to referral to community services.

4. This assumes family members are available to help and also places the burden on the client's wife to arrange for assistance.

Classification

Competency Category:	Nurse-Client Relationship
Taxonomic Level:	Application
Client Type:	Families
Age Group:	Adult

References

Thelan, L. A., Urden, L. D., Lough, M. E., & Stacy, K. M. (1998), p. 817.

Taylor, C., Lillis, C., & LeMone, P. (1997), p. 1067.

29. correct answer: 1

1. A return demonstration by the client provides an opportunity to practise under supervision and to evaluate learning.
2. There is no opportunity for evaluation of learning.
3. This is not as effective as a demonstration and supervised practice of the procedure.
4. This is not as effective as a demonstration and supervised practice of the procedure.

Classification

Competency Category:	Health Promotion
Taxonomic Level:	Application
Client Type:	Families
Age Group:	Adult

References

Thelan, L. A., Urden, L. D., Lough, M. E., & Stacy, K. M. (1998), p. 769.

Hudak, C. M., Gallo, B. M., & Morton, P. G. (1998), p. 701.

30. correct answer: 4

1. This diminishes/devalues his concerns and does not provide any concrete assistance.
2. This suggestion may be premature. The expertise of an occupational therapist is necessary to determine if this is a realistic goal for the client.
3. The expertise of an occupational therapist, not a social worker, is necessary to determine if this is a realistic goal for the client.
4. The expertise of an occupational therapist is necessary to determine if this is a realistic goal for the client.

Classification

Competency Category:	Rehabilitative Care
Taxonomic Level:	Application
Client Type:	Families
Age Group:	Adult

References

DuGas, B. W., & Knor, E. R. (1995), pp. 80-81.

Taylor, C., Lillis, C., & LeMone, P. (1997), p. 184.

7

31. correct answer: 1

1. In the immediate post-burn period, the ABC's of trauma care dictate priorities. With facial burns, it is necessary to closely monitor respiratory status and rule out inhalation injury.

2. Although increasingly important as fluid shift occurs over the next 24 hours, this is not the priority at this time.

3. Assessment of the client's respiratory status is the priority. This should wait until the assessment is completed.

4. Assessment of the client's respiratory status is the priority.

Classification

Competency Category:	Curative/Supportive Care
Taxonomic Level:	Critical Thinking
Client Type:	Individuals
Age Group:	Adult

References

Smeltzer, S. C., & Bare, B. G. (1996), p. 1551.
Burton, G. G., Hodgkin, J. E., & Ward, J. J. (1997), p. 1092.

32. correct answer: 3

1. This is not the most efficient option. The nurse will have to remove her isolation wear and perhaps waste opened dressings, according to principles of asepsis.

2. Medication dose should not be reduced. Flamazine needs to be applied liberally on burns to be effective.

3. This is an appropriate delegation of task, since it involves medication.

4. Participating in activities related to medication administration is not within the responsibilities and duties of a unit clerk.

Classification

Competency Category:	Professional Practice
Taxonomic Level:	Critical Thinking
Client Type:	Individuals
Age Group:	Adult

References

Taylor, C., Lillis, C., & LeMone, P. (1997), pp. 304-305.
Williams, B. R., & Baer, C. L. (1998), p. 44.

33. correct answer: 4

1. Removing the dressings quickly will not reduce discomfort and may traumatize the wound.

2. Although this does provide the client with some control over her care, having the client remove her dressings will not reduce her discomfort.

3. The onset of Morphine occurs within 5 minutes when administered by PCA pump. The dressing change should be done when the peak effect is achieved (i.e., 20 minutes).

4. **Soaking the dressings for at least 10 minutes will soften the exudate which causes the dressing to adhere to the wound bed.**

Classification

Competency Category:	Curative/Supportive Care
Taxonomic Level:	Knowledge/Comprehension
Client Type:	Individuals
Age Group:	Adult

References

Ignatavicius, D. D., Workman, M. L., & Mishler, M. A. (1995), p. 1997.

Smeltzer, S. C., & Bare, B. G. (1996), p. 1565.

34. correct answer: 3

1. Since the client has been on Morphine via PCA with no adverse effects, her level of consciousness should not be a concern at this point.

2. If the client has been stable on Morphine, vital signs should not be affected by the change in route.

3. **This would be the primary concern, as adequate pain control must be ensured with a change in route of administration.**

4. Having been on Morphine, the change to oral route should not affect the client's oxygenation.

Classification

Competency Category:	Curative/Supportive Care
Taxonomic Level:	Knowledge/Comprehension
Client Type:	Individuals
Age Group:	Adult

References

Lewis, S. M., Collier, I. C., & Heitkemper, M. M. (1996), p. 104.

Smeltzer, S. C., & Bare, B. G. (1996), p. 192.

7

35. correct answer: 3

1. This response excludes the significant other in the process of caring for the client.

2. This response does not invite participation of the client's significant other in her care.

3. **This response welcomes the significant other and provides an opportunity to involve the significant other in the client's care in preparation for discharge.**

4. The exercise program should not be delayed as it is an important aspect of rehabilitation. This response does not invite participation of the client's significant other in her care.

Classification

Competency Category: Rehabilitative Care
Taxonomic Level: Application
Client Type: Families
Age Group: Adult

References

Lewis, S. M., Collier, I. C., & Heitkemper, M. M. (1996), p. 552.
Smeltzer, S. C., & Bare, B. G. (1996), pp. 1581-1582.

36. correct answer: 3

1. Although the role of caffeine in hypertension is controversial, one cup of coffee a day is not considered excessive.

2. Because alcohol may raise blood pressure, moderate consumption is advised. The consumption described is not significant with respect to hypertension.

3. **Nicotine constricts blood vessels, therefore elevating her BP.**

4. A family history of prostatic cancer would not increase the risk of hypertension.

Classification

Competency Category: Curative/Supportive Care
Taxonomic Level: Application
Client Type: Individuals
Age Group: Adult

References

Phipps, W. J., Cassmeyer, V. L., Sands, J. K., & Lehman, M. K. (1995), pp. 920-922.
Smeltzer, S. C., & Bare, B. G. (1996), pp. 745-752.

37. correct answer: 4

1. The potassium level is elevated, and should be normal (3.5-5.5 mEq/L), or could be decreased, with the use of chlorothiazide (Diuril).

2. The client's BP remains unchanged and chlorothiazide (Diuril) should lower her BP.

3. The client's weight should decrease as diuresis occurs.

4. **An overall deficit indicates diuresis, an expected outcome with chlorothiazide (Diuril).**

Classification

Competency Category:	Curative/Supportive Care
Taxonomic Level:	Application
Client Type:	Individuals
Age Group:	Adult

References

Phipps, W. J., Cassmeyer, V. L., Sands, J. K., & Lehman, M. K. (1995), p. 923.

Smeltzer, S. C., & Bare, B. G. (1996), p. 747.

38. correct answer: 3

1. Nurse Smith is demonstrating insecurity and is being defensive.

2. By stating what has happened in the past, Nurse Smith is being defensive.

3. **By agreeing to try sample menus, Nurse Smith is indicating a receptiveness to new ideas.**

4. It is within the nurse's scope of practice to provide sample menus to a client without the dietitian's help.

Classification

Competency Category:	Professional Practice
Taxonomic Level:	Affective
Client Type:	Individuals
Age Group:	Adult

References

Canadian Nurses Association. *Code of Ethics for Registered Nurses* (1997), p. 20.

Taylor, C., Lillis, C., & LeMone, P. (1997), pp. 84-86.

39. correct answer: 3

1. Stating that "It's only the blood pressure" devalues the importance of the constructive feedback and indicates that Nurse Jones does not understand the importance of BP assessment in relation to antihypertensives.

2. Defensively stating "I already knew that" implies BP assessment is not important.

3. **Stating that "I must remember that" and asking if blood pressure needs to be taken prior to administering antihypertensive medication indicate acceptance of constructive feedback.**

4. Not checking the blood pressure because it is in the normal range shows a lack of knowledge regarding antihypertensive medications.

Classification

Competency Category: Professional Practice
Taxonomic Level: Affective
Client Type: Individuals
Age Group: Adult

References

Taylor, C., Lillis, C., & LeMone, P. (1997), pp. 375-377.
Arnold, E., & Boggs, K. U. (1995), pp. 527-529.

40. correct answer: 3

1. When the child sits upright, gravity facilitates drainage from only the upper segments and bronchi.

2. A supine position is used to promote drainage from only the anterior lobes.

3. **Frequent changes of position are recommended during postural drainage and percussion to facilitate drainage from all major lung segments.**

4. Positioning the child with the chest lower than the abdomen is used to remove secretions from only the lower lobes and bronchi.

Classification

Competency Category: Curative/Supportive Care
Taxonomic Level: Knowledge/Comprehension
Client Type: Families
Age Group: Child & Adolescent

References

Pillitteri, A. (1999), pp. 1121-1122, 1156-1157.
Wong, D. L. (1995), pp. 1349, 1441.

41. correct answer: 4

1. Discussing the techniques for postural drainage may not address the parents' specific needs. They may understand the treatment but require assistance in adapting their approach to make it more acceptable to the child.

2. Postural drainage treatments are critical to the daily management of cystic fibrosis. Due to the chronic nature of the illness, it is necessary that family members are actively involved in the treatment.

3. Postural drainage and percussion are important aspects of the treatment and should be done 2-4 times daily, to prevent infection. Delaying treatment will increase the risk of respiratory infections.

4. **Teaching should be individualized to address the specific needs of the learner once they have been assessed.**

Classification

Competency Category:	Curative/Supportive Care
Taxonomic Level:	Application
Client Type:	Families
Age Group:	Child & Adolescent

References

Pillitteri, A. (1999), pp. 1121-1122, 1156-1157.
Wong, D. L. (1995), p. 193.
Friedman, M. M. (1998), pp. 486-487.

42. correct answer: 4

1. The Apgar Score is used immediately after birth to evaluate the newborn's adjustment to extra-uterine life.

2. The Snellen Screening Test is used to measure visual acuity.

3. An Intelligence Quotient Test measures cognitive ability.

4. **The Denver Developmental Screening Test is a widely used screening test that evaluates personal/social, fine motor, language, and gross motor skills in children from 2 weeks to 6 years of age.**

Classification

Competency Category:	Curative/Supportive Care
Taxonomic Level:	Knowledge/Comprehension
Client Type:	Families
Age Group:	Child & Adolescent

References

Pillitteri, A. (1999), pp. 947, 951.
Wong, D. L. (1995), pp. 278-280.

7

43. correct answer: 3

1. Constipation indicates a need for fewer enzymes which the parents are meeting by decreasing the amount administered.

2. It is recommended that pancreatic enzymes be increased to match food intake; therefore, further teaching is unnecessary.

3. **The parents need additional teaching so that they are instructed to administer pancreatic enzymes with all meals and snacks rather than in the morning and at bedtime.**

4. The parents are correct in increasing the enzymes since large, bulky stools are suggestive of impaired absorption. This does not suggest a need for additional teaching.

Classification

Competency Category:	Health Promotion
Taxonomic Level:	Application
Client Type:	Families
Age Group:	Child & Adolescent

References

Pillitteri, A. (1999), pp. 1156-1157.

Wong, D. L. (1995), p. 1439.

44. correct answer: 4

1. The parents' reaction is a normal response. Many parents who have children with a chronic illness experience "chronic sorrow"; that is, times when parental sorrow and grief resurface. The nurse should not assume or tell the parents they are depressed.

2. Telling the family they are coping well belittles their concern by providing false reassurance.

3. Research has shown that after 1 year, many families do find living with cystic fibrosis less stressful. The nurse needs to recognize that each family may react somewhat differently and not compare these parents with "most people."

4. **Social support may help decrease feelings of isolation. Families who share their burden with family members or other helpers outside the family tend to demonstrate higher levels of family functioning.**

Classification

Competency Category:	Nurse-Client Relationship
Taxonomic Level:	Application
Client Type:	Families
Age Group:	Child & Adolescent

References

Pillitteri, A. (1999), pp. 1157-1158.

Wong, D. L. (1995), pp. 956-957.

45. correct answer: 2

1. The nurse needs a policy approved by the nurse's employing agency, not by an external agency such as the local hospital.

2. **When the nurse is assigned to work outside an area of present competence, the nurse's immediate supervisor should be contacted for direction.**

3. Carrying out the procedure is wrong because it could result in injury to the client.

4. The lack of a policy should be discussed at the local level initially before contacting a provincial/territorial association.

Classification

Competency Category:	Professional Practice
Taxonomic Level:	Application
Client Type:	Families
Age Group:	Child & Adolescent

References

Canadian Nurses Association. (1997), *Code of Ethics for Registered Nurses*, p. 20.

Hall, J. K. (1996), pp. 162-163.

46. correct answer: 1

1. **Determining if the parents respond immediately to infant cries assesses their facilitation of the development of trust in the infant.**

2. Asking about the use of a pacifier determines if the parents are meeting the baby's comfort needs, and would not necessarily facilitate the development of trust in the infant.

3. Asking about the infant's feeding pattern would be more important than the types of food when determining the development of trust.

4. Asking about the types of toys provided would assess how the parents view the baby's cognitive levels rather than the level of trust.

Classification

Competency Category:	Curative/Supportive Care
Taxonomic Level:	Critical Thinking
Client Type:	Families
Age Group:	Child & Adolescent

References

Pillitteri, A. (1999), pp. 758-759.

Wong, D. L. (1995), p. 523.

7

47. correct answer: 1

1. Decreased urinary output, sunken fontanels, and decreased skin turgor are common symptoms of dehydration in the infant.

2. With hypervolemia, urinary output would increase, not decrease.

3. Although hyponatremia is a component of dehydration syndrome, the nurse's assessment data do not include serum electrolyte results.

4. In water intoxication, urinary output increases and vomiting and diarrhea occur.

Classification

Competency Category:	Curative/Supportive Care
Taxonomic Level:	Knowledge/Comprehension
Client Type:	Families
Age Group:	Child & Adolescent

References

Pillitteri, A. (1999), pp. 1297-1299.
Wong, D. L. (1995), pp. 1210-1211.

48. correct answer: 1

1. Elevating the crib sides fully at all times prevents the child from rolling out and also prevents other children from climbing into the crib.

2. For safety reasons, infant mobiles must hang at least 30 cm above the face so that the infant cannot become entangled in them.

3. A bubble top is unnecessary for a 3-month-old child, but is used with toddlers who are able to climb.

4. It is unsafe to have a pillow in the crib as it could smother the child.

Classification

Competency Category:	Illness/Injury Prevention
Taxonomic Level:	Application
Client Type:	Families
Age Group:	Child & Adolescent

References

Pillitteri, A. (1999), p. 999.
Wong, D. L. (1995), pp. 1210-1211.

49. correct answer: 1

1. In order to feel comfortable, the parents need to be assisted and to have "hands on" experience in bathing their baby several times.

2. Ensuring that staff bathe the baby would not help the parents overcome their fears.

3. Having follow-up supervision at home would indicate a lack of trust in the parents' ability to bathe their baby.

4. Having the parents demonstrate their bathing technique is part of assessment, and not an intervention that promotes hygiene.

Classification

Competency Category:	Health Promotion
Taxonomic Level:	Application
Client Type:	Families
Age Group:	Child & Adolescent

References

Pillitteri, A. (1999), pp. 790-791.

Boyd, M. D., Graham, B. A., Gleit, C. J., & Whitman, N. I. (1998), pp. 224-225.

50. correct answer: 1

1. Caring includes giving help to parents when they appear less able to cope with child care activities such as feeding.

2. The nurse should not place the responsibility of contacting the social worker on the parents.

3. Visiting time should be determined by the parents. The nurse should consider the parents' level of fatigue.

4. Offering the parents general reading material on parenting skills is not the best way of demonstrating a caring attitude.

Classification

Competency Category:	Nurse-Client Relationship
Taxonomic Level:	Critical Thinking
Client Type:	Families
Age Group:	Child & Adolescent

References

Haber, J., Krainovich-Miller, B., McMahon, A. L., & Price-Hoskins, P. (1997), p. 214.

Wong, D. L. (1995), pp. 1109-1110.

7

51. correct answer: 2

1. Religious affiliation and marital status have little influence on menopause.

2. **In cultures where attitudes toward aging are positive, menopause is less stressful. In cultures that value youth and reproductivity, menopause may be stressful. A woman's expectations/feelings strongly influence her emotional state during menopause.**

3. Her financial status has no bearing on menopause. Her husband's attitude toward her could have a positive or negative influence.

4. Socioeconomic status does not influence menopause. The number of children she has had might be useful information only if it strongly influenced her self-esteem in the maternal role.

Classification

Competency Category:	Curative/Supportive Care
Taxonomic Level:	Application
Client Type:	Individuals
Age Group:	Adult

References

Lowdermilk, D. L., Perry, S. E., & Bobak, I. M. (1997), pp. 1131-1133.

Phipps, W. J., Cassmeyer, V. L., Sands, J. K., & Lehman, M. K. (1995), pp. 266-267, 280-281.

52. correct answer: 3

1. This entry does not mention the client's loss of pleasure with sexual relations.

2. The client has not stated that she is frigid.

3. **This entry into the nursing notes is appropriate; all information is charted correctly.**

4. This entry does not mention the client's loss of pleasure with sexual relations, and repeats information about fear of becoming pregnant.

Classification

Competency Category:	Curative/Supportive Care
Taxonomic Level:	Application
Client Type:	Individuals
Age Group:	Adult

References

Lowdermilk, D. L., Perry, S. E., & Bobak, I. M. (1997), pp. 1158-1160.

Phipps, W. J., Cassmeyer, V. L., Sands, J. K., & Lehman, M. K. (1995), pp. 267-269.

53. correct answer: 2

1. This is a closed-ended question, and will not determine if the client has benefited from the medication. Also, the client may not know what the side effects are.

2. **This open-ended question allows the client to tell the nurse about benefits and side effects of the medication.**

3. This is a closed-ended question and will not determine the side effects the client may be experiencing.

4. This is a closed-ended question and will not determine if the client is experiencing side effects.

Classification

Competency Category:	Nurse-Client Relationship
Taxonomic Level:	Application
Client Type:	Individuals
Age Group:	Adult

References

Taylor, C., Lillis, C., & LeMone, P. (1997), p. 252.

DuGas, B. W., & Knor, E. R. (1995), p. 412.

54. correct answer: 4

1. The client has not mentioned anxiety or changes in body image.

2. The client may be indirectly seeking knowledge about causes of pain, but there is no indication of changes in her sexual patterns. The change is in her sexual function.

3. The client has not indicated that her self-esteem has been affected by her changing sexual patterns. She has identified pain as the problem.

4. **Hormonal changes at menopause cause dryness and thinning of the vaginal mucous membrane, leading to pain during intercourse. This can be overcome with the use of water-soluble lubricants.**

Classification

Competency Category:	Curative/Supportive Care
Taxonomic Level:	Application
Client Type:	Individuals
Age Group:	Adult

References

Lowdermilk, D. L., Perry, S. E., & Bobak, I. M. (1997), p. 1159.

Phipps, W. J., Cassmeyer, V. L., Sands, J. K., & Lehman, M. K. (1995), p. 268.

7

55. correct answer: 3

1. The client's readiness to learn must be assessed prior to implementing the plan.

2. Evaluation should be done after implementation, and can be arranged once the client has thought about and reviewed the material.

3. **Using materials the client understands is essential in ensuring comprehension and retention of information.**

4. Asking the client about her current knowledge of the topic is part of the assessment of learning needs.

Classification

Competency Category:	Health Promotion
Taxonomic Level:	Application
Client Type:	Individuals
Age Group:	Adult

References

Taylor, C., Lillis, C., & Lemone, P. (1997), p. 396.

Boyd, M. D., Graham, B. A., Gleit, C. J., & Whitman, N. I. (1998), p. 213.

56. correct answer: 2

1. Collecting pamphlets does not guarantee that the nurse will read the material.

2. **Attending a workshop will enhance the nurse's knowledge of menopause and aging, and will provide suitable preparation for caring for the client.**

3. Talking to a co-worker is not the most appropriate action because each person's experience with menopause is different.

4. Asking the client to share what she knows about menopause does nothing to expand the nurse's professional knowledge base.

Classification

Competency Category:	Professional Practice
Taxonomic Level:	Application
Client Type:	Individuals
Age Group:	Adult

References

Taylor, C., Lillis, C., & LeMone, P. (1997), pp. 14-18.

DuGas, B. W., & Knor, E. R. (1995), p. 124.

57. correct answer: 4

1. The nurse must remain with the client until medications have been taken. If the nurse has not witnessed the client taking the medication, it cannot be recorded as given.

2. This is non-therapeutic communication with a confused, irritable client and may further aggravate the client's anxiety.

3. This is deceptive and should be avoided if possible. It is difficult to ensure that the client takes her full dose of medication if it is administered in this manner.

4. **This is the most appropriate initial action. Clients with stage 2 Alzheimer's have periods of irritability and short-term memory loss. Often after a cooling down period they are compliant. Approaching the client in a calm and friendly manner is most likely to obtain cooperation.**

Classification

Competency Category:	Nurse-Client Relationship
Taxonomic Level:	Application
Client Type:	Individuals
Age Group:	Adult of Advanced Age

References

Taylor, C., Lillis, C., & LeMone, P. (1997), p. 613.

Matteson, M. A., McConnell, E. S., Linton A. D., & Mahlmeister, L. (1997) pp. 742-747.

58. correct answer: 3

1. It is appropriate for the nurse to do health teaching about birth control.

2. The nurse is being judgmental. This is not a therapeutic response.

3. **The nurse provides information on the various methods. She also takes the opportunity to do health teaching about preventing sexually transmitted diseases.**

4. Sixteen years of age is the age of majority in Canada. Parental consent is not needed.

Classification

Competency Category:	Health Promotion
Taxonomic Level:	Application
Client Type:	Individuals
Age Group:	Child & Adolescent

References

Lowdermilk, D. L., Perry, S. E., & Bobak, I. M. (1999), p. 121.

Thompson, E. D. (1995), p. 108.

Wong, D. L. (1995), pp. 879-885.

7

59. correct answer: 3

1. This may assist with keeping the air clean of impurities but clean air has not been shown to prevent SIDS.
2. Reduced body temperature has not been shown to potentiate SIDS. Overheating has been associated with SIDS.
3. **Recent studies have shown an increased incidence of SIDS in infants who sleep on their stomachs. There is no evidence that sleeping on the back is harmful to healthy infants.**
4. Use of an infant monitor will not prevent SIDS.

Classification

Competency Category:	Health Promotion
Taxonomic Level:	Critical Thinking
Client Type:	Groups, Populations, Communities
Age Group:	Not Applicable

References

Lowdermilk, D. L., Perry, S. E., & Bobak, I. M. (1999), p. 574.
Olds, S. B., London, M. L., & Ladewig, P. W. (1996), p. 873.
Thompson, E. D. (1995), pp. 888-889.

60. correct answer: 2

1. The colleague is denying the nurse the opportunity to express her feelings and this may hinder the grieving process.
2. **Talking about it will assist the nurse to grieve and conveys a caring, non-judgmental and supportive attitude.**
3. The colleague is encouraging the nurse to avoid expressing her feelings at this time, which may hinder the grieving process.
4. Giving false reassurance will block communication and will not allow the nurse to express her feelings.

Classification

Competency Category:	Health Promotion
Taxonomic Level:	Knowledge/Comprehension
Client Type:	Individuals
Age Group:	Child & Adolescent

References

Boyd, M. A., & Nihart, M. A. (1998), p. 1023.
Antai-Otong, D. (1995), p. 121.

61. correct answer: 4

1. Planning of daily activities may be an effective method of coping with stress. However, this is not the most effective strategy as it does not involve the client in selecting a stress reduction method.

2. The client may be reassured by knowing that a nurse will visit him at home. However, this does not allow him to develop strategies to cope with stress.

3. Although rest is desirable, the client needs to deal effectively with stress in order to allow for rest.

4. **Having the client practise an effective stress reduction method in the hospital reinforces healthy coping strategies.**

Classification

Competency Category:	Health Promotion
Taxonomic Level:	Knowledge/Comprehension
Client Type:	Individuals
Age Group:	Older Adult

References

Taylor, C., Lillis, C., & LeMone, P. (1997), pp. 768-769.
DuGas, B. W., & Knor, E. R. (1995), pp. 202-206.

62. correct answer: 1

1. **Tuberculosis is spread by airborne transmission through inhalation of droplets. Small droplets remain suspended in the air.**

2. A mask must be worn when in the client's room because small droplets remain suspended in the air.

3. Spread is by airborne transmission, not through skin contact.

4. Spread is by airborne transmission, not through skin contact.

Classification

Competency Category:	Illness/Injury Prevention
Taxonomic Level:	Knowledge/Comprehension
Client Type:	Individuals
Age Group:	Adult

References

Smeltzer, S. C., & Bare, B. G. (1996), pp. 495-501.
Phipps, W., Cassmeyer, V., Sands, J., & Lehman, M. (1995), p. 359.

7

63. correct answer: 1

1. **Determining the stage of labour which is necessary for choice of analgesia.**

2. Although having a support person is important during labour, the client has requested an analgesic.

3. This information is important; however, the determination of the stage of labour is the first priority.

4. This information is important; however, the determination of the stage of labour is the first priority.

Classification

Competency Category:	Curative/Supportive Care
Taxonomic Level:	Critical Thinking
Client Type:	Individuals
Age Group:	Adult

References

Pillitteri, A. (1999), pp. 507-508.

Lowdermilk, D. L., Perry, S. E., & Bobak, I. M. (1999), pp. 313-315.

64. correct answer: 3

1. This would be an effective teaching method if the client was provided with an opportunity to ask questions and review the information before she leaves the hospital. In addition, the nurse has not assessed the client's knowledge of her condition.

2. This would be an effective teaching method if the client was provided with an opportunity to ask questions and review the information. The nurse should first assess the client's knowledge of her condition. Also, the client may not effectively learn from videos. It would be necessary to first determine what she would prefer.

3. **The nurse, in collaboration with the client, assesses the client's learning needs and readiness to learn, and then forms a teaching plan.**

4. The client would first need to be informed about an antenatal home care program before she could state her perceptions of her own responsibilities while in it.

Classification

Competency Category:	Curative/Supportive Care
Taxonomic Level:	Application
Client Type:	Individuals
Age Group:	Adult

References

Pillitteri, A. (1999), pp. 412-413, 416-417.

Craven, R. F., & Hirnle, C. (1996), pp. 500, 508.

65. correct answer: 2

1. These symptoms are not associated with hypothermia.

2. **These are classic signs of hypovolemia. A common cause of hypovolemia is unreplaced fluid loss.**

3. Disorientation and hypotension are not associated with pain.

4. Hypotension is not associated with anxiety.

Classification

Competency Category:	Curative/Supportive Care
Taxonomic Level:	Knowledge/Comprehension
Client Type:	Individuals
Age Group:	Adult

References

Lewis, S. M., Collier, I. C., & Heitkemper, M. M. (1996), p. 392.

Smeltzer, S. C., & Bare, B. G. (1996), p. 404.

66. correct answer: 2

1. The airway remains in place until swallowing has been demonstrated. The most effective position is prone to allow for drainage of secretions.

2. **The airway remains in place until swallowing has been demonstrated. Prone positioning and head turned to the side allows for drainage of secretions.**

3. The airway remains in place until swallowing has been demonstrated. Suctioning could cause hemorrhage.

4. This will not help clear up secretions or blockage and open up the airway. An oxygen saturation of 94% does not warrant physician intervention.

Classification

Competency Category:	Curative/Supportive Care
Taxonomic Level:	Application
Client Type:	Individuals
Age Group:	Child & Adolescent

References

Smeltzer, S. C., & Bare, B. G. (1996), p. 466.

Wong, D. L. (1995), p. 1383.

67. correct answer: 1

1. **These are signs of neurovascular compromise; this is a medical emergency.**

2. Repositioning will not aleviate neurovascular compromise.

3. Analgesia may mask symptoms of pain in neurovascular compromise.

4. Removing the cast is not an independent nursing action.

Classification

Competency Category:	Curative/Supportive Care
Taxonomic Level:	Knowledge/Comprehension
Client Type:	Individuals
Age Group:	Adult

References

Smeltzer, S. C., & Bare, B. G. (1996), p. 1852.

Nettina, S. M. (1996), p. 845.

7

68. correct answer: 1

1. **Bloating and vomiting are signs of a blocked nasogastric tube and its patency should be verified.**

2. There should be a doctor's order for removing the nasogastric tube.

3. Bloating and vomiting are signs of a blocked nasogastric tube; administering an antiemetic will not alleviate the cause of these symptoms.

4. The intervention could potentially rupture the incision line and may cause aspiration of stomach contents.

Classification

Competency Category:	Curative/Supportive Care
Taxonomic Level:	Knowledge/Comprehension
Client Type:	Individuals
Age Group:	Older Adult

References

Taylor, C., Lillis, C., & LeMone, P. (1997), p. 1187.

Thelan, L. A., Urden, L. D., Lough, M. E., & Stacy, K. M. (1998), p. 966.

69. correct answer: 2

1. The head of the bed is elevated to 30 degrees; in this position the enlarged abdomen would cause pressure on the diaphragm.

2. **Elevating the head of the bed to 45 degrees facilitates breathing as it allows the abdominal organs to drop, hence greater expansion of the rib cage and lowering of the diaphragm.**

3. The client would be lying on her back with hips flexed at 90 degrees which would push the abdominal organs toward the diaphragm. This is normally a birthing position.

4. In this position, the client lies flat and on one side, supported by pillows. This would exert pressure on the abdomen, creating further discomfort for the client.

Classification

Competency Category:	Curative/Supportive Care
Taxonomic Level:	Knowledge/Comprehension
Client Type:	Individuals
Age Group:	Adult

References

Taylor, C., Lillis, C., & LeMone, P. (1997), pp. 1034-1036.

Ignatavicius, D. D., Workman, M. L., & Mishler, M. A. (1995), pp. 697-698.

70. correct answer: 2

1. The drainage would appear blood tinged yellow or pink. It consists of a mixture of blood and serum or plasma.

2. **It consists of plasma and is clear and watery.**

3. It consists of a large number of red blood cells and looks like blood.

4. The drainage would be cloudy, opaque, and may contain pus. It is thick because it consists of white blood cells and necrotic tissue. It could also be yellow or green.

Classification

Competency Category:	Curative/Supportive Care
Taxonomic Level:	Knowledge/Comprehension
Client Type:	Individuals
Age Group:	Adult

References

Taylor, C., Lillis, C., & LeMone, P. (1997), p. 701.

DuGas, B. W., & Knor, E. R. (1995), pp. 1065-1066.

71. correct answer: 3

1. This answer is incorrect.

2. This answer is incorrect.

3. **60mg x 15 kg = 900mg/24 hours ÷ 4 = 225 mg q 6h**

4. This answer is incorrect.

Classification

Competency Category:	Curative/Supportive Care
Taxonomic Level:	Application
Client Type:	Individuals
Age Group:	Child & Adolescent

References

Canadian Pharmacists Association. (1999), p. 356.

Karch, A. (1999), p. 258.

7

72. correct answer: 2

1. IV normal saline will not help this client, who is in an acute asthmatic attack. Hydration will help liquify secretions but it is not the priority.

2. **As the client is in a severe asthmatic attack and demonstrating respiratory distress, oxygen therapy should be started immediately and be monitored by pulse oximeter.**

3. This drug has anti-inflammatory properties and will decrease the edema in the respiratory tract. However, the client needs the oxygen first.

4. The combination of oxygen and a bronchodilator will improve oxygenation. Oxygen is the first priority.

Classification

Competency Category: Curative/Supportive Care
Taxonomic Level: Critical Thinking
Client Type: Individuals
Age Group: Adult

References

Lewis, S. M., Collier, I. C., & Heitkemper, M. M. (1996), pp. 686-688.
Smeltzer, S. C., & Bare, B. G. (1996), pp. 518-520.

73. correct answer: 2

1. The client's current use of the PCA pump is ineffective in managing her pain. Telling the client that an antidote is available reinforces her misunderstanding regarding the possibility of an overdose.

2. **Reinforcing to the client how and when to use the PCA pump will correct her inappropriate use of the PCA pump, reassure her on its use, and manage her pain more effectively.**

3. Although the client has not been using the PCA pump appropriately, the client should not stop using the PCA pump. It is the nurse's responsibility to assess and evaluate the client's response to the medication.

4. Although the client has not been using the PCA pump appropriately, the nurse would not administer a large dose of morphine by this route to a client using a PCA pump.

Classification

Competency Category: Curative/Supportive Care
Taxonomic Level: Application
Client Type: Individuals
Age Group: Adult

References

Varrichio, C., Pierce, M., Walker, C. L., & Ades, T. B. (1997), p. 175.
Eisenhauer, L. A., Nichols, L. W., & Bergon, F. W. (1998), p. 325.

74. correct answer: 3

1. Only 0.9% normal saline should be administered with blood products to prevent hemolysis of the red blood cells.

2. Two registered nurses must first verify the information on the chart and on the blood product.

3. **Altered vital signs or other adverse reactions are early indications of transfusion reaction.**

4. The intravenous infusion should be maintained until the possibility of delayed reactions is ruled out.

Classification

Competency Category:	Curative/Supportive Care
Taxonomic Level:	Application
Client Type:	Individuals
Age Group:	Older Adult

References

Craven, R. F., & Hirnle, C. (1996), pp. 569-570.

Taylor, C., Lillis, C., & LeMone, P. (1997), pp. 1425-1427.

75. correct answer: 1

1. **Use of accessory muscles is evidence of respiratory distress. Tachypnea and decreased air entry occur when the lung tissue becomes consolidated.**

2. Tachycardia and barrel chest are signs of chronic obstructive pulmonary disease. Nasal flaring is associated with acute respiratory distress.

3. Tachypnea and pursed-lip breathing are signs of chronic obstructive pulmonary disease. A productive cough is a desired treatment outcome of pneumonia.

4. Increased anterior/posterior diameter, clubbing, and wheezing are signs of chronic obstructive pulmonary disease.

Classification

Competency Category:	Curative/Supportive Care
Taxonomic Level:	Application
Client Type:	Individuals
Age Group:	Adult of Advanced Age

References

Lewis, S. M., Collier, I. C., & Heitkemper, M. M. (1996), pp. 574-576.

Smeltzer, S. C., & Bare, B. G. (1996), pp. 476-477.

7

76. correct answer: 1

1. **Relaxed posture and a calm, low voice, along with acknowledging the client's feelings will reassure the client that the nurse is there to help her and decrease some of her anxiety. Often a crisis can be diverted by early verbal intervention.**

2. The p.r.n. medication may ultimately be required but only after the nurse has assessed that the client requires it to maintain control.

3. This would be very threatening to the client, increase her anxiety, and escalate the situation.

4. This is not an appropriate intervention when there has not been an incident of violence.

Classification

Competency Category:	Curative/Supportive Care
Taxonomic Level:	Critical Thinking
Client Type:	Individuals
Age Group:	Adult

References

Stuart, G. W., & Laraia, M. T. (1998), p. 629.

Boyd, M. A., & Nihart, M. A. (1998), p. 1040.

77. correct answer: 3

1. It is important that the nurse not erect barriers to communication by assuming how the client feels.

2. A barrier is erected by avoiding discussion of the grief.

3. **If a client chooses not to share feelings, the nurse conveys a willingness to be available. Effective listening techniques help the client move through the grieving process.**

4. The nurse should acknowledge the client's feelings. By offering medication at this time, the client's feelings are discounted.

Classification

Competency Category:	Curative/Supportive Care
Taxonomic Level:	Application
Client Type:	Individuals
Age Group:	Older Adult

References

Potter, P. A., & Perry, A. G. (1995), pp. 502-503.

Craven, R. F., & Hirnle, C. (1996), pp. 1469-1470.

78. correct answer: 2

1. The client will begin ambulation with assistance as soon as possible, likely the first day after surgery.

2. **This is the usual progression in the rehabilitation process of clients with an open reduction and internal fixation of the femur.**

3. Although rehabilitation will be initiated with the physician's order, this does not address the client's concern.

4. Rehabilitation will start while the client is still experiencing some discomfort. Ambulation always begins with some assistance.

Classification

Competency Category:	Rehabilitative Care
Taxonomic Level:	Application
Client Type:	Individuals
Age Group:	Older Adult

References

Smeltzer, S. C., & Bare, B. G. (1996), p. 1928.

Phipps, W., Cassmeyer, V., Sands, J., & Lehman, M. (1995), p. 2201.

79. correct answer: 2

1. Wastage must be witnessed by the nurse co-signing it.

2. **Wastage should be witnessed and co-signed by a second nurse. It is within the scope of practice of the student nurse to co-sign the wastage.**

3. This is not good practice because the nurse co-signing the wastage cannot be certain that the clear fluid placed in the cupboard is Demerol.

4. This is not a practical solution as the supervisor or staff from another floor may not be immediately available. This would cause undue suffering of the client as the injection would be delayed.

Classification

Competency Category:	Professional Practice
Taxonomic Level:	Knowledge/Comprehension
Client Type:	Individuals
Age Group:	Adult

References

DuGas, B. W., & Knor, E. R. (1995), p. 1103.

Taylor, C., Lillis, C., & LeMone, P. (1997), p. 609.

7

80. correct answer: 2

1. 20 mg is an excessive dose and would cause severe respiratory depression.

2. **The nurse should question this order as 20 mg is an excessive dose and would cause severe respiratory depression.**

3. Although the sublingual route would be preferred because of its rapid onset of action, the 20 mg is an excessive dose and would cause severe respiratory depression.

4. 20 mg is an excessive dose and would cause severe respiratory depression. The order needs to be clarified with the physician prior to notifiying pharmacy.

Classification

Competency Category: Professional Practice
Taxonomic Level: Application
Client Type: Individuals
Age Group: Adult

References

Phipps, W., Cassmeyer, V., Sands, J., & Lehman, M. (1995), p. 1972.
Nursing 98 Books (1998), p. 469.

81. correct answer: 1

1. **The colleague has failed to meet the standards of practice by landmarking the injection site improperly. The standard of safety has been violated. The public has the right to expect that a nurse is capable of carrying out her duties competently and with a clear mind. She is jeopardizing client safety working while impaired and should be removed from duty.**

2. The nurse should be concerned about whether her colleague drew up the correct medication or dose and therefore should stop the medication from being administered. An impaired nurse should be confronted about her behaviour and removed from client care areas.

3. This would be very upsetting to the client and would put her colleague on the defensive for the later interaction.

4. The nurse should not administer any injection which she has not drawn up herself. The colleague should be removed from the client care area and the nursing supervisor or the appropriate authority notified.

Classification

Competency Category: Professional Practice
Taxonomic Level: Application
Client Type: Individuals
Age Group: Not Applicable

References

Grant, A. E., & Ashman, A. A. (1997), p. 63.
Canadian Nurses Association. *Code of Ethics for Registered Nurses* (1997), pp. 26-27.

82. correct answer: 4

1. Although the chaplain may be able to counsel the client, at her request, it is unlikely that this discipline would have all the appropriate information regarding the options for the client to consider.

2. A conference may identify the client's support system and may be an important step in helping her come to a decision. However, the father has indicated that he does not wish to be involved. In addition, the client needs to explore options available to her with a professional with expertise in this area.

3. It would be important for the community health nurse to visit the client as soon as possible. However, the client should receive the necessary information before she leaves the hospital.

4. **If the hospital does not have a social worker with expertise in counselling clients in this area, a community agency would need to be contacted. The nurse should provide support and guidance to the client but would likely be limited in describing the process for considering actual options.**

Classification

Competency Category:	Professional Practice
Taxonomic Level:	Application
Client Type:	Families
Age Group:	Child & Adolescent

References

Lowdermilk, D. L., Jensen, M. D., & Perry, S. E. (1999), pp. 923-924.

Arnold, E., & Boggs, K. U. (1995), p. 521.

7

83. correct answer: 2

1. This would not be the nurse's initial intervention in order to implement a successful community program. Home visits to individuals would not necessarily meet the needs of the community.

2. **The nurse invites stakeholders to develop a plan, set goals, and follow up. Including representatives of the community increases the likelihood that the initiative will be successful. The nurse also recognizes the importance of elders in this cultural context.**

3. Arranging clinic visits for individuals would not necessarily meet the needs of the community. This intervention does not facilitate recognition of cultural practices.

4. This intervention is premature and does not consider cultural practices nor include involvement of key stakeholders.

Classification

Competency Category: Health Promotion
Taxonomic Level: Application
Client Type: Groups, Populations, Communities
Age Group: Not Applicable

References

Armentrout, G. (1998), p. 87.
Williams, S. R. (1995), p. 259.

84. correct answer: 4

1. This is an example of primary prevention of illness.

2. This is an opportunity for early diagnosis of illness and is an example of secondary prevention.

3. This is an opportunity for early diagnosis of illness and is an example of secondary prevention.

4. **This activity is directed at promoting general health, and maintaining and improving nutritional status.**

Classification

Competency Category: Health Promotion
Taxonomic Level: Critical Thinking
Client Type: Groups, Populations, Communities
Age Group: Not Applicable

References

DuGas, B. W., & Knorr, E. R. (1995), p. 66.
Stewart, M. J. (1995), pp. 478-479.

85. correct answer: 4

1. Does not identify readiness of the target group to be receptive to information provided and, thereby, does not reflect the principles of teaching and learning. Reliability of the strategy is in question; will the letter reach home and will it be read?

2. Does not address the basic problem and ignores principles of teaching and learning.

3. Information given without addressing readiness to learn does not follow principles of teaching and learning.

4. **This strategy best reflects the principles of teaching and learning. This will give the nurse the opportunity to provide information to the target group and assess readiness to learn about the problem as well as gauge potential compliance.**

Classification

Competency Category:	Health Promotion
Taxonomic Level:	Application
Client Type:	Groups, Populations, Communities
Age Group:	Not Applicable

References

Spradley, B. W., & Allender, J. A. (1996), pp. 310-315.

Hunt, R., & Zurek, E. L. (1997), pp. 194-202.

86. correct answer: 3

1. A newborn with a fever needs to be seen immediately by a physician or in the Emergency because it is likely related to an infection that requires treatment.

2. Use of topical alcohol could cause extreme cooling which is a shock to an immature nervous system. Alcohol can be absorbed by the skin or the fumes inhaled in toxic amounts, further compromising the child.

3. **Taking the temperature of newborns by axilla is a safe and effective method. Taking rectal and oral temperatures are not recommended in newborns due to risk of injury.**

4. Aspirin is contraindicated for use in children due to its association with Reye's syndrome.

Classification

Competency Category:	Health Promotion
Taxonomic Level:	Application
Client Type:	Groups, Populations, Communities
Age Group:	Adult

References

Wong, D. L. (1995), p. 1163.

Pillitteri, A. (1999), pp. 1048-1049.

7

87. correct answer: 4

1. This is an incorrect response as the nurse has not answered the question that was asked.

2. This is wrong information as lactation is not a reliable choice of contraception.

3. The use of oral contraception during lactation is not the first choice of contraception as the estrogen contained in the medication may reduce milk supply and pass into breastmilk.

4. **This is correct. Women may ovulate but not menstruate while breastfeeding, thus it is not reliable in ensuring they will not get pregnant.**

Classification

Competency Category:	Health Promotion
Taxonomic Level:	Knowledge/Comprehension
Client Type:	Groups, Populations, Communities
Age Group:	Adult

References

Pillitteri, A. (1999), p. 111.

Riordan, J., & Averbach, K. G. (1999), p. 695.

88. correct answer: 3

1. While this is true, it is a derogatory response to their concerns. It may discourage them from asking further questions and is unlikely to promote breastfeeding.

2. This is not true. If adequately nourished, a teenager should be able to produce sufficient breastmilk.

3. **There is only a minimal difference between adolescent and adult breastmilk. If the teenager is adequately nourished, she can produce sufficient milk to nourish her baby.**

4. This is incorrect. If adequately nourished, a teenager should be able to produce sufficient breastmilk. However, partial breastfeeding is preferred to not breastfeeding at all.

Classification

Competency Category:	Health Promotion
Taxonomic Level:	Application
Client Type:	Groups, Populations, Communities
Age Group:	Child & Adolescent

References

Pillitteri, A. (1999), p. 663.

Riordan, J., & Averbach, K. G. (1999), pp. 526-533.

89. correct answer: 2

1. Although this is valid, proper handwashing is the most effective method to prevent the transmission of infection.

2. **Handwashing after using the toilet and handling diapers is the single most effective method of preventing the risk of spreading bacterial gastrointestinal infection.**

3. This is a preventative measure and will help decrease transmission of gastrointestinal bacteria. However, handwashing is the most effective method of preventing transmission of gastro-intestinal bacteria.

4. There is no immunization for bacterial gastroenteritis.

Classification

Competency Category:	Health Promotion
Taxonomic Level:	Knowledge/Comprehension
Client Type:	Groups, Populations, Communities
Age Group:	Not Applicable

References

Wong, D. L. (1995), p. 1165.

Smith, C. M., & Maurer, F. A. (1995), p. 503.

90. correct answer: 1

1. **Acknowledges the clients' concerns and provides support and encouragement.**

2. Places blame and responsibility on the client and does not address the voiced concerns.

3. This is inaccurate information and misleading to the clients.

4. The nurse should be able to deal with the issue at hand.

Classification

Competency Category:	Health Promotion
Taxonomic Level:	Affective
Client Type:	Groups, Populations, Communities
Age Group:	Older Adult

References

Murray, R. B., & Zestner, J. P. (1997), p. 618.

Lewis, S. M., Collier, I. C., & Heitkemper, M. M. (1996), pp. 889-891.

7

91. correct answer: 2

1. There is no rationale for delaying the immunization schedule. There are very few absolute contraindications for immunization (e.g., anaphylaxis, encephalopathy to last vaccine).

2. **There is no reason to interrupt immunization. There are very few absolute contraindications for immunization (e.g., anaphylaxis, encephalopathy to last vaccine).**

3. The nurse should not defer this matter to the physician. The nurse should advise the mother to continue immunization based on her knowledge.

4. Knowledge of certain illnesses present in the community would not change the importance of having her child immunized in a timely manner.

Classification

Competency Category:	Illness/Injury Prevention
Taxonomic Level:	Application
Client Type:	Families
Age Group:	Child & Adolescent

References

Hitchcock, J. E., & Thomas, S. A. (1999), p. 468.

Clemen-Stone, S., Eigsti, D. G., & McGuire, S. L. (1995), p. 544.

92. correct answer: 2

1. Placing the client on a cardiac monitor needs to be done but not before attending to the acute respiratory difficulty.

2. **Based on this assessment, this is the priority intervention due to his low oxygen saturation and cyanosis.**

3. This client's respiratory status is the priority, not completing the physical assessment.

4. An electrocardiogram needs to be done but not before attending to the acute respiratory difficulty.

Classification

Competency Category:	Curative/Supportive Care
Taxonomic Level:	Application
Client Type:	Individuals
Age Group:	Older Adult

References

Burton, G. G., Hodgkin, J. E., & Ward, J. J. (1997), p. 275.

Harkness, G. A., & Dincher, J. R. (1996), p. 533.

93. correct answer: 4

1. The potential for symptoms of infection is less likely in this time period.

2. Deep vein thrombosis develops later. Adult clients are at greater risk.

3. Intake and output in a pediatric surgical client must be monitored but fluid imbalance is not the most significant potential problem.

4. **Compartment syndrome is the most serious postoperative complication of those stated that could occur during the stated time frame.**

Classification

Competency Category:	Curative/Supportive Care
Taxonomic Level:	Knowledge/Comprehension
Client Type:	Individuals
Age Group:	Child & Adolescent

References

Smeltzer, S. C., & Bare, B. G. (1996), p. 1917.
Bates, G. F. (1997), p. 464.

94. correct answer: 2

1. Assessing cognitive ability is not the immediate priority.

2. **Morphine is a respiratory depressant. Respiratory depression will compromise the client and should be assessed first.**

3. The PCA pump must be programmed according to the physician's orders but is not the immediate priority.

4. The effectiveness of PCA to control pain must be assessed but is not the immediate priority.

Classification

Competency Category:	Curative/Supportive Care
Taxonomic Level:	Critical Thinking
Client Type:	Individuals
Age Group:	Adult of Advanced Age

References

Miller, C. A. (1999), p. 112.
Karch, A. (1999), p. 817.

7

95. correct answer: 3

1. Although nutritional intake is critical for burn healing, this response does not explore or address why Melissa is not eating.

2. This does not address the reasons for the client's failure to eat.

3. Ballet dancers are at risk for eating disorders. Female adolescents may be more concerned with control of weight than nutrition. Further interventions to help the client meet her nutritional needs will be required once the problem is explored.

4. Total parenteral nutrition is not indicated at this time. The problem has not been explored and less invasive interventions should be attempted.

Classification

Competency Category:	Curative/Supportive Care
Taxonomic Level:	Critical Thinking
Client Type:	Individuals
Age Group:	Child & Adolescent

References

Dudek, S. G. (1997), pp. 334-335.

Taylor, C., Lillis, C., & LeMone, P. (1997), p. 1167.

96. correct answer: 2

1. Incorrect as it is less than the required amount for his weight.

2. 0.3 mg x 40 kg = 12.0 mg for the whole day. The nurse will give 2 doses of 6 mg.

3. 12 mg is the total daily dose.

4. Incorrect as this is double the daily dose.

Classification

Competency Category:	Curative/Supportive Care
Taxonomic Level:	Application
Client Type:	Individuals
Age Group:	Child & Adolescent

References

Colombaro, G. C. (1998), p. 133.

Canadian Pharmacists Association. (1999), p. 1573.

97. correct answer: 2

1. Turning off the infusion pump will jeopardize the patency of the venous site.

2. **The priority intervention is to reset the infusion to the ordered rate to prevent fluid overload.**

3. This is not the first priority but would be done at a later time.

4. Reporting an error should be done only after the safety of the client is ensured and the infusion rate is adjusted.

Classification

Competency Category: Curative/Supportive Care
Taxonomic Level: Application
Client Type: Individuals
Age Group: Child & Adolescent

References

Taylor, C., Lillis, C., & LeMone, P. (1997), p. 660.
Potter, P. A., & Perry, A. G. (1999), p. 613.

98. correct answer: 2

1. Lorazepam is administered for anxiety. The client is exhibiting signs of respiratory distress.

2. **This is the treatment of choice as he is asthmatic and needs a bronchodilator to relieve his symptoms. Bronchodilation is the therapeutic effect of this drug.**

3. Nitroglycerine improves coronary blood flow and relieves symptoms of angina. These symptoms do not justify this medication.

4. This medication is administered for pain. The client is exhibiting signs of respiratory distress.

Classification

Competency Category: Curative/Supportive Care
Taxonomic Level: Application
Client Type: Individuals
Age Group: Older Adult

References

Skidmore-Roth, L. (1997), pp. 83-84.
Burton, G. G., Hodgkin, J. E., & Ward, J. J. (1997), p. 1026.

7

99. correct answer: 2

1. Peak plasma levels for meperidine occur within approximately 45 minutes. The client should be experiencing some relief of pain at this time.

2. **The average adult dose of meperidine IM is 50 to 150 mg, q 3-4h. Considering the client's weight and his continued pain, a larger dose of medication can be given safely. It is the nurse's responsibility to evaluate the client's response to medication, relay information when the desired effect of medication is not attained, and intervene on the client's behalf.**

3. The client is in pain. The medication dosage is ineffective within the ordered time frame and needs to be increased.

4. The client is in pain. The medication dosage is ineffective within the ordered time frame and needs to be increased. It is the nurse's responsibility to seek an order change in this situation.

Classification

Competency Category:	Curative/Supportive Care
Taxonomic Level:	Critical Thinking
Client Type:	Individuals
Age Group:	Adult

References

Canadian Pharmacists Association. (1999), p. 476.

Karch, A. (1999), p. 733.

100. correct answer: 1

1. **The oliguric phase of acute renal failure can include congestive heart failure.**

2. Hypovolemia is a finding in the diuretic phase of acute renal failure.

3. Postural hypotension is a manifestation possible in the diuretic phase of acute renal failure.

4. Clients in the oliguric phase of acute renal failure are prone to fluid volume excess, not deficit.

Classification

Competency Category:	Curative/Supportive Care
Taxonomic Level:	Critical Thinking
Client Type:	Individuals
Age Group:	Older Adult

References

Phipps, W. J., Cassmeyer, V. L., Sands, J. K., & Lehman, M. K. (1995), pp. 1662-1663.

Smeltzer, S. C., & Bare, B. G. (1996), pp. 1194-1195.

101. correct answer: 3

1. Clients in the oliguric phase are on fluid restrictions and most are not able to tolerate oral feedings.

2. Clients only need to be weighed daily.

3. **The side rails should be left up for safety reasons because drowsiness is a symptom of acute renal failure.**

4. Strict bed rest is recommended during the oliguric phase of acute renal failure.

Classification

Competency Category:	Curative/Supportive Care
Taxonomic Level:	Knowledge/Comprehension
Client Type:	Individuals
Age Group:	Older Adult

References

Phipps, W. J., Cassmeyer, V. L., Sands, J. K., & Lehman, M. K. (1995), pp. 1662-1663.

Smeltzer, S. C., & Bare, B. G. (1996), pp. 1193-1195.

102. correct answer: 2

1. It is important to turn and position these clients because they are prone to skin breakdown; however, it is not necessary to do this q 1h.

2. **Urinary output is crucial in the management of acute renal failure. All observations of the client's state of hydration need to be recorded so that hour-to-hour and day-to-day comparisons can be made.**

3. It is important to do deep breathing exercises as these clients can progress to CHF; however, it is not necessary to do this q 1h.

4. Edema may be present but it is not necessary to assess q 1h.

Classification

Competency Category:	Curative/Supportive Care
Taxonomic Level:	Application
Client Type:	Individuals
Age Group:	Older Adult

References

Phipps, W. J., Cassmeyer, V. L., Sands, J. K., & Lehman, M. K. (1995), pp. 1662-1663.

Smeltzer, S. C., & Bare, B. G. (1996), pp. 1193-1195.

7

103. correct answer: 3

1. This response is inappropriate because the nurse should not leave an apprehensive client who is hemorrhaging.

2. This response is inappropriate because the nurse is suggesting the client is at fault, without addressing the client's apprehension.

3. **This is the most appropriate response because the nurse is responding to the client's feelings and shows support in a calm manner.**

4. This response is inappropriate because it does not take the client's anxiety into account.

Classification

Competency Category:	Nurse-Client Relationship
Taxonomic Level:	Application
Client Type:	Individuals
Age Group:	Older Adult

References

DuGas, B. W., & Knor, E. R. (1995), pp. 410-411.

Taylor, C., Lillis, C., & LeMone, P. (1997), p. 377.

104. correct answer: 3

1. Changes should be reported immediately. Charting may not be done until late in the shift.

2. Rechecking the float nurse's assessment is an inappropriate use of the charge nurse's time.

3. **Reviewing with the float nurse what should be assessed and reported is important because it ensures that the float nurse will assess and report relevant observations immediately.**

4. Asking the nurse working in the next room to be available to the float nurse will not ensure that the float nurse will assess and report relevant observations immediately.

Classification

Competency Category:	Curative/Supportive Care
Taxonomic Level:	Knowledge/Comprehension
Client Type:	Individuals
Age Group:	Older Adult

References

DuGas, B. W., & Knor, E. R. (1995), pp. 334-335.

Taylor, C., Lillis, C., & LeMone, P. (1997), pp. 248-249.

105. correct answer: 3

1. Providing milkshakes t.i.d. is inappropriate because clients in acute renal failure should eat a low protein, high carbohydrate, high fat diet. Milkshakes are high in protein and therefore contraindicated.

2. Ensuring her privacy during meals is inappropriate because people tend to eat better in a social group setting than by themselves.

3. **Appetite is often best in the morning and deteriorates gradually throughout the day. Therefore, a high-calorie breakfast should be encouraged.**

4. Water between meals would ensure fluid intake, but would not provide the required calories.

Classification

Competency Category:	Curative/Supportive Care
Taxonomic Level:	Critical Thinking
Client Type:	Individuals
Age Group:	Older Adult

References

Phipps, W. J., Cassmeyer, V. L., Sands, J. K., & Lehman, M. K. (1995), pp. 1662-1663.

Smeltzer, S. C., & Bare, B. G. (1996), pp. 1194-1195.

106. correct answer: 1

1. **Appropriate nursing interventions for an unconscious client include talking with the client while providing nursing care, explaining procedures, and identifying who is in the room.**

2. The nurse should not discuss the client's condition by talking "over" him. The nurse should assume that the client can hear all conversations in his presence.

3. There is no special need to speak slowly or clearly to an unconscious client. It is inappropriate to use the family to pressure the client to perform activities.

4. Hearing is the last sensation lost with unconscious clients. Tactile stimulation is also important, but not at the expense of auditory stimulation; hence, whispering is an inappropriate approach.

Classification

Competency Category:	Curative/Supportive Care
Taxonomic Level:	Application
Client Type:	Families
Age Group:	Child & Adolescent

References

Phipps, W. J., Cassmeyer, V. L., Sands, J. K., & Lehman, M. K. (1995), pp. 1934-1935.

Smeltzer, S. C., & Bare, B. G. (1996), p. 1723.

7

107. correct answer: 3

1. Taping the hole contravenes principles of asepsis.

2. The high concentration of glucose in the amino acid solution stimulates high levels of insulin production. Suddenly removing the glucose source can precipitate a dangerous hypoglycemic reaction.

3. **Infusing Dextrose 10% is the most appropriate action since it temporarily replaces the glucose source during the time the nurse awaits the delivery of the new bag.**

4. The lipids would be an inappropriate replacement for the glucose and it would be incorrect to increase the rate of lipids being infused without a physician's order.

Classification

Competency Category:	Curative/Supportive Care
Taxonomic Level:	Critical Thinking
Client Type:	Individuals
Age Group:	Child & Adolescent

References

Phipps, W. J., Cassmeyer, V. L., Sands, J. K., & Lehman, M. K. (1995), pp. 1959-1962.

Smeltzer, S. C., & Bare, B. G. (1996), pp. 876-880.

108. correct answer: 2

1. Resting splints prevent contracture deformity (foot drop), but do not promote circulation.

2. **Contracting and relaxing the leg muscles, even through passive means, promotes circulation in the lower extremities.**

3. Administering warm packs to the calves is not an effective or safe measure to promote circulation.

4. Elevating the foot of the client's bed decreases arterial flow.

Classification

Competency Category:	Curative/Supportive Care
Taxonomic Level:	Application
Client Type:	Individuals
Age Group:	Child & Adolescent

References

Phipps, W. J., Cassmeyer, V. L., Sands, J. K., & Lehman, M. K. (1995), pp. 1937-1938.

Smeltzer, S. C., & Bare, B. G. (1996), pp. 1721-1723.

109. correct answer: 2

1. Good lighting is essential to assess the oxygen status of a ventilated client; therefore, lights should not be dimmed.

2. **Linen which is wrinkle-free prevents skin breakdown which is a risk for the unconscious client.**

3. A prone position is not safe practice for a spinal cord injured, unconscious client because of the risk of aspiration.

4. Although the client is unconscious, his privacy should still be maintained during personal care.

Classification

Competency Category:	Illness/Injury Prevention
Taxonomic Level:	Application
Client Type:	Individuals
Age Group:	Child & Adolescent

References

Phipps, W. J., Cassmeyer, V. L., Sands, J. K., & Lehman, M. K. (1995), pp. 1935-1937.

Smeltzer, S. C., & Bare, B. G. (1996), p. 1723.

110. correct answer: 2

1. Documenting this situation does not have any direct effect on promoting a safe practice environment.

2. **Advising the nursing supervisor is the best means to promote a safe practice environment. It notifies the nurse supervisor of the changing conditions on the unit and also sets in motion a plan for getting more help.**

3. It would be inappropriate to leave the bedside of the unstable client for an extended period.

4. It would be inappropriate for the practical nurse/nursing assistant to provide care for a client who is not stable.

Classification

Competency Category:	Professional Practice
Taxonomic Level:	Critical Thinking
Client Type:	Individuals
Age Group:	Child & Adolescent

References

Canadian Nurses Association. (1997), *Code of Ethics for Registered Nurses*, p. 20.

DuGas, B. W., & Knor, E. R. (1995), p. 124.

7

111. correct answer: 3

1. The timing is incorrect. Hot water from a kettle should not be used, especially with a geriatric client. Thinner skin layers of the older client increase the risk for burn.

2. This is incorrect as boiling water will promote burning and maceration of the skin. Also, the hot water bottle should not be kept in place for more than 30 minutes.

3. **This is the correct application of heat from a hot water bottle.**

4. Using tap water is correct. However, it should not be kept in place for more than 30 minutes. Older adults will have decreased sensation to skin surfaces.

Classification

Competency Category:	Curative/Supportive Care
Taxonomic Level:	Knowledge/Comprehension
Client Type:	Families
Age Group:	Adult of Advanced Age

References

Potter, P. A., & Perry, A. G. (1999), pp. 1120-1124.
Craven, R. F., & Hirnle, C. (1996), p. 1104.

112. correct answer: 2

1. It is standard practice to flush the device with 1 to 3 ml of normal saline q 8h.

2. **This is important to prevent backflow of blood into the catheter, which could cause a clot to form.**

3. Standard replacement of the device is every 48 to 72 hours.

4. Cleansing of the injection port is usually done with alcohol. Iodine preparations are more commonly used with central venous lines.

Classification

Competency Category:	Curative/Supportive Care
Taxonomic Level:	Knowledge/Comprehension
Client Type:	Individuals
Age Group:	Older Adult

References

Phillips, D. L. (1997), p. 362.
Weinstein, S. M. (1997), p. 219.

113. correct answer: 4

1. Although bedrest is indicated for the first 24 hours following a transuretheral resection of the prostate, it is more important to control the bleeding through increasing the rate of the continuous bladder irrigation.

2. There is no indication that the tubing is blocked, which is when milking the tubing would be done.

3. This action is indicated only when drainage stops and a blockage is suspected.

4. **It is the nurse's judgment to adjust the irrigation fluid rate to maintain a colourless or light-pink drainage return.**

Classification

Competency Category:	Curative/Supportive Care
Taxonomic Level:	Knowledge/Comprehension
Client Type:	Individuals
Age Group:	Older Adult

References

Ignatavicius, D. D., Workman, M. L., & Mishler, M. A. (1995), p. 2270.

Phipps, W., Cassmeyer, V., Sands, J., & Lehman, M. (1995), pp. 1789-1790.

114. correct answer: 3

1. Doctor's orders need to be activated based on individual client assessments.

2. Although this is a consideration, it is not a priority and further assessment needs to be carried out prior to removing the tube.

3. **These are appropriate assessments that indicate return of bowel function and support removal of the NG tube.**

4. This is not a relevant consideration since the gastrointestinal tract is not sterile.

Classification

Competency Category:	Curative/Supportive Care
Taxonomic Level:	Knowledge/Comprehension
Client Type:	Individuals
Age Group:	Older Adult

References

Craven, R. F., & Hirnle, C. (1996), pp. 1253-1259.

Potter, P. A., & Perry, A. G. (1995), pp. 1101-1105.

7

115. correct answer: 4

1. Overloading the circulatory system with excessive intravenous fluids will cause hypertension, coughing and pulmonary edema.

2. This is a local complication. It is characterized by lack of flow as well as difficulty administering the infusion rate.

3. These are not signs of infection. The nurse needs more assessment data in order to identify either systemic or local infection.

4. **This complication occurs most frequently with central lines. Smaller amounts of air are significant when using this method of infusion as opposed to peripheral sites.**

Classification

Competency Category:	Curative/Supportive Care
Taxonomic Level:	Knowledge/Comprehension
Client Type:	Individuals
Age Group:	Adult of Advanced Age

References

Craven, R. F., & Hirnle, C. (1996), p. 560.

Smeltzer, S. C., & Bare, B. G. (1996), pp. 243-244.

116. correct answer: 4

1. The pamphlet is a good reference but this alone is not enough to ensure compliance.

2. Verbal communication is important but will not ensure continuity of care.

3. Although the client may understand hip precautions, it is important to see how he adapts in his own home environment.

4. **The physiotherapist can assess the home and advise the client regarding safety features and adaptive measures. The physiotherapist can also assess the client's compliance.**

Classification

Competency Category:	Curative/Supportive Care
Taxonomic Level:	Critical Thinking
Client Type:	Families
Age Group:	Older Adult

References

Hoeman, S. P. (1996), p. 118.

Matteson, M. A., McConnell, E. S., & Linton, A. D. (1997), p. 863.

117. correct answer: 3

1. Although it is important for the client to have peer support, the client should be involved in selecting the method to stop smoking from the variety of options available in the community. Client involvement will increase potential for success.

2. This method of stopping smoking has not been known to be successful. The client should be involved in selecting the method to stop smoking from the variety of options available in the community. Client involvement will increase potential for success.

3. **A variety of smoking cessation programs are available in the community. Smoking cessation programs found in the community have better success rates. The client should be involved in selecting the method to stop smoking from the variety of options available in the community. Providing referral information is a responsibility of the nurse.**

4. Nicotine patches are contraindicated for clients with angina. While nicotine patches have a certain degree of success, this option does not allow client involvement in selecting the smoking cessation method.

Classification

Competency Category:	Rehabilitative Care
Taxonomic Level:	Application
Client Type:	Individuals
Age Group:	Adult

References

Hoeman, S. P. (1996), p. 406.

Clemen-Stone, S., Eigsti, D. G., & McGuire, S. L. (1995), p. 625.

7

118. correct answer: 4

1. Limiting fluids is an intervention in bladder retraining; however, limiting fluids to 1 litre a day is too restrictive.

2. A goal of bladder retraining is to increase the interval between voidings in order to increase bladder volume. Having the client void small amounts every hour will not achieve this goal.

3. Self-catheterization is an intervention specifically for long-term problems of incomplete bladder emptying.

4. **By postponing the urge to void, the client consciously learns to control his bladder. A goal of bladder retraining is to increase the interval between voidings in order to increase bladder volume.**

Classification

Competency Category:	Rehabilitative Care
Taxonomic Level:	Knowledge/Comprehension
Client Type:	Individuals
Age Group:	Adult

References

Hoeman, S. P. (1996), pp. 439-440.

Ignatavicius, D. D., Workman, M. L., & Mishler, M. A. (1995), p. 2063.

119. correct answer: 2

1. This is unrealistic. The client has rights under the mental health legislation, and can only be detained if there is sufficient evidence that he poses a danger to himself or others. The nurse is making a promise she cannot keep and could betray the client's trust.

2. **Families need support, encouragement, and counselling to deal with the changing roles and relationships that mental illness may precipitate. The social worker is the appropriate resource to assist the family.**

3. This option may be premature at this time. This would be disruptive for the family and would not preserve the integrity of the family unit.

4. Although this will be useful later, the nurse should recognize that the family is in crisis now and needs support.

Classification

Competency Category:	Rehabilitative Care
Taxonomic Level:	Application
Client Type:	Families
Age Group:	Adult

References

Haber, J., Krainovich-Miller, B., McMahon, A. L., & Price-Hoskins, P. (1997), p. 360.

Johnson, B. S. (1997), p. 624.

120. correct answer: 2

1. The physician is not in a position to independently establish hospital policy. It may be a courtesy to advise the physician of the visit but unnecessary to have an order.

2. **The nurse is advocating for the client. The unit manager is the appropriate level of authority to consult with when there are no written policies to guide practice.**

3. The nurse is not in a position to authorize the visit without consulting with the unit manager.

4. It is the nurse's responsibility to advocate for the client in the absence of policy.

Classification

Competency Category:	Professional Practice
Taxonomic Level:	Application
Client Type:	Individuals
Age Group:	Adult

References

Hogstel, M. O. (1995), p. 39.

Canadian Nurses Association. (1997), *Code of Ethics for Registered Nurses*, p. 20.

121. correct answer: 2

1. The tray should be prepared at the same physical location as the dressing, for example, the client's room. Preparing the tray elsewhere increases the potential of contamination of the tray.

2. **The centre of the wound is considered cleaner than the outward borders. Cleansing from clean to dirty prevents introducing organisms into the wound.**

3. The gloves are necessary for dressing removal because they act as a barrier protecting both the nurse as well as the client.

4. The purpose of the Montgomery straps/tie tapes is to minimize skin breakdown from repeated removal of tape. The Montgomery straps/tie tapes should be changed only when soiled or when not adhering properly.

Classification

Competency Category:	Curative/Supportive Care
Taxonomic Level:	Knowledge/Comprehension
Client Type:	Individuals
Age Group:	Adult

References

Rosdahl, C. B. (1995), p. 647.

Craven, R. F., & Hirnle, C. (1996), p. 1093.

7

122. correct answer: 3

1. Vital signs should be taken to assess the client's status. It is not the client's responsibility to monitor the practice of health care providers.

2. The unregulated health care provider should not have administered medications because it is not within their scope of practice. They should inform the nurse of their concerns about clients.

3. **It is important that the nurse clarify her role and responsibilities and that the unregulated health care provider should not have administered medications because it is not within their scope of practice. The nurse is accountable for ensuring client safety and reporting the incident for follow-up.**

4. The nurse should know that unregulated health care providers should not be administering medications to clients.

Classification

Competency Category: Professional Practice
Taxonomic Level: Application
Client Type: Individuals
Age Group: Adult

References

Canadian Nurses Association. (1997), *Code of Ethics for Registered Nurses*, p. 19.

Grant, A. E., & Ashman, A. A. (1997), p. 179.

123. correct answer: 4

1. This may increase the damage to skin that is already traumatized.

2. Although this is an important consideration, it is not the most immediate concern.

3. Powder should be avoided as it tends to cake and become an irritant.

4. **Relief of pressure will ensure adequate blood flow to the affected area and promote healing as well as preventing further damage.**

Classification

Competency Category: Curative/Supportive Care
Taxonomic Level: Application
Client Type: Individuals
Age Group: Adult

References

Smeltzer, S. C., & Bare, B. G. (1996), p. 344.

Lewis, S. M., Collier, I. C., & Heitkemper, M. M. (1996), p. 523.

124. correct answer: 4

1. This response is not culturally sensitive.
2. Not a timely option during this stage of labour.
3. This response is not culturally sensitive and may instill guilt.
4. **This acknowledges the client's cultural practices and beliefs.**

Classification

Competency Category: Nurse-Client Relationship
Taxonomic Level: Application
Client Type: Families
Age Group: Adult

References

Pillitteri, A. (1999), p. 496.

Canadian Nurses Association. (1997), *Everyday Ethics: Putting the Code into Practice*, p. 15.

125. correct answer: 4

1. This approach does not resolve the client's problem.
2. This approach may not meet the client's needs; the client needs privacy.
3. Valuing the client's cultural rituals is essential. Offering a private room may be unrealistic.
4. **Expressing understanding of the client's needs facilitates a trusting relationship. Providing a quiet room meets the need for culturally sensitive care to the client.**

Classification

Competency Category: Nurse-Client Relationship
Taxonomic Level: Affective
Client Type: Individuals
Age Group: Older Adult

References

Riley, J. W., Balzer. (1996), pp. 111-123.

Giger, J. N., & Davidhizar, R. E. (1995), pp. 7-14.

7

126. correct answer: 1

1. **Correct administration of oral contraceptives should begin on the fifth day of the menstrual cycle.**

2. Nausea, weight gain and breast tenderness are common side effects and will subside after one or two cycles.

3. It is recommended to stop smoking entirely as there is an increased risk of cardiovascular problems with oral contraceptive medications.

4. It is recommended that the missed dosage be taken as soon as possible and another form of birth control be used for the remainder of the cycle.

Classification

Competency Category:	Nurse-Client Relationship
Taxonomic Level:	Critical Thinking
Client Type:	Individuals
Age Group:	Child & Adolescent

References

Lilley, L. L., & Aucker, R. S. (1999), pp. 437, 448.

Williams, B. R., & Baer, C. L. (1998), p. 559.

127. correct answer: 4

1. The term "isolated" would need further explanation to the parents.

2. The terminology in this response is too technical.

3. This response has no bearing on the child's present infectious condition.

4. **This statement is correct because it uses simple terms, and is repetitious to reinforce learning.**

Classification

Competency Category:	Illness/Injury Prevention
Taxonomic Level:	Application
Client Type:	Families
Age Group:	Child & Adolescent

References

Wong, D. L. (1995), pp. 776-779, 783-785, 1164-1165.

Thompson, E. D. (1995), pp. 606-607.

128. correct answer: 3

1. Setting up suction equipment may be required but the nurse would have to leave the client unsupervised while doing this, and this client should not be left unsupervised.

2. Restraint may cause further injury to the individual due to the strong muscle activity involved in seizures.

3. **By staying with the client while waiting for help to arrive, the nurse can try to prevent injury and monitor the client.**

4. The use of touch in a therapeutic manner is important, but the priority is to stay with the client and call for help.

Classification

Competency Category:	Illness/Injury Prevention
Taxonomic Level:	Application
Client Type:	Individuals
Age Group:	Adult of Advanced Age

References

Phipps, W. J., Cassmeyer, V. L., Sands, J. K., & Lehman, M. K. (1995), p. 1963.

Smeltzer, S. C., & Bare, B. G. (1996), pp. 1783-1785.

129. correct answer: 2

1. There should be no need for this extent of mobility assistance.

2. **There may be adequate resources currently in place for the family, or for the nurse to build on, once assessed.**

3. A nurse may already be making visits or the client may be involved in some other program.

4. This presumes that the family should take over the care, and represents an unfair responsibility to place on the family.

Classification

Competency Category:	Rehabilitative Care
Taxonomic Level:	Knowledge/Comprehension
Client Type:	Individuals
Age Group:	Older Adult

References

Taylor, C., Lillis, C., & LeMone, P. (1997), pp. 201-204.

DuGas, B. W., & Knor, E. R. (1995), pp. 214-215.

7

130. correct answer: 2

1. Renting a hospital bed is unnecessary because he can use his own bed.

2. **Buying loose-fitting clothes will accommodate the cast around the waist and leg.**

3. Because he has a hip spica with an extension to one leg, he is unable to bend at the waist and cannot use a wheelchair.

4. A home care worker is not necessary as his parents will be taught how to safely turn him.

Classification

Competency Category:	Rehabilitative Care
Taxonomic Level:	Application
Client Type:	Families
Age Group:	Child & Adolescent

References

Shapiro, P. J. (1995), p. 684.

Nettina, S. M. (1997), p. 342.

Book 2
Rationales

1. correct answer: 2

1. Delusional ideas show a disturbance in the client's thought processes, not his intellectual capacity.

2. **Delusional ideas are a response to emotional needs and their purpose is to reduce stress.**

3. Delusional ideas are a distortion in cognitive functions and do not provide any etiological explanation.

4. A person with delusional ideas does not necessarily undergo a personality change.

Classification

Competency Category:	Curative/Supportive Care
Taxonomic Level:	Critical Thinking
Client Type:	Individuals
Age Group:	Adult

References

Boyd, M. A., & Nihart, M. A. (1998), p. 424.

Varcarolis, E. M. (1998), p. 632.

2. correct answer: 3

1. Observation is not an intervention that will prevent violence.

2. It is not the nurse's responsibility to convince the client and his family; the nurse must support their decisions.

3. **Identifying needs and expressing feelings reduces stress and facilitates problem solving.**

4. It is preferable to include other family members in planning care without excluding the client.

Classification

Competency Category:	Illness/Injury Prevention
Taxonomic Level:	Knowledge/Comprehension
Client Type:	Families
Age Group:	Adult

References

Boyd, M. A., & Nihart, M. A. (1998), p. 391.

Haber, J., Krainovich-Miller, B., McMahon, A. L., & Price-Hoskins, P. (1997), p. 595.

3. correct answer: 1

1. **Recognizing that the client is afraid of intimacy helps the nurse respect his pace and needs when integrating him into the group.**

2. The hallucinations are not the most important factor in the decision to integrate the client into the group.

3. The relationship of trust is basic to any therapeutic intervention, but is not specific to the decision to integrate the client into a support group.

4. The medications are part of the treatment and do not exclude group activities.

Classification

Competency Category:	Nurse-Client Relationship
Taxonomic Level:	Knowledge/Comprehension
Client Type:	Individuals
Age Group:	Adult

References

Haber, J., Krainovich-Miller, B., McMahon, A. L., & Price-Hoskins, P. (1997), p. 594.

Varcarolis, E. M. (1998), p. 630.

7

4. correct answer: 3

1. Having much interaction could be anxiogenic for the client.

2. Encouraging the client to leave his room does not necessarily help improve his self-esteem.

3. **Tasks that the client can perform successfully promote his self-esteem.**

4. Compliments can increase emotional dependence without increasing self-esteem. They can also be viewed as additional stress and, consequently, a source of anxiety.

Classification

Competency Category:	Curative/Supportive Care
Taxonomic Level:	Knowledge/Comprehension
Client Type:	Individuals
Age Group:	Adult

References

Boyd, M. A., & Nihart, M. A. (1998), p. 266.

Haber, J., Krainovich-Miller, B., McMahon, A. L., & Price-Hoskins, P. (1997), pp. 633-634.

5. correct answer: 3

1. Although very useful, the learning objectives emerge from data collection. Thus, they are not developed at the first stage.

2. The support group is necessary for social reintegration. However, its purpose is not primarily to learn basic skills.

3. **The nurse first collects data with the client that will help him meet his needs more effectively.**

4. The nurse has no guarantee that she will meet the client's needs when she prepares a list of learning needs.

Classification

Competency Category:	Health Promotion
Taxonomic Level:	Application
Client Type:	Individuals
Age Group:	Adult

References

Boyd, M. A., & Nihart, M. A. (1998), pp. 413-414.

Haber, J., Krainovich-Miller, B., McMahon, A. L., & Price-Hoskins, P. (1997), p. 397.

6. correct answer: 3

1. Telling the client what he must do will not necessarily result in changes in his behaviour.

2. This strategy increases the client's dependence on his family and may arouse negative feelings in the client and his family.

3. **Developing a reminder system with the client increases the possibility that this strategy will suit him and that he will use it.**

4. The diary will not help the client achieve the desired objective.

Classification

Competency Category:	Curative/Supportive Care
Taxonomic Level:	Knowledge/Comprehension
Client Type:	Individuals
Age Group:	Adult

References

Boyd, M. A., & Nihart, M. A. (1998), p. 300.

Haber, J., Krainovich-Miller, B., McMahon, A. L., & Price-Hoskins, P. (1997), p. 597.

7. correct answer: 2

1. Vital signs and body mass are important data that are part of the physical examination.

2. **The health assessment and physical examination are essential tools for screening since they enable identification of factors that could have negative effects on the pregnancy.**

3. Blood and urine test results are important data that are part of the physical examination.

4. It is important to know the couple's expectations, but this is not a priority during the first visit. Moreover, the couple is more concerned about the pregnancy than labour and delivery.

Classification

Competency Category:	Illness/Injury Prevention
Taxonomic Level:	Critical Thinking
Client Type:	Families
Age Group:	Adult

References

Bobak, I. M., Lowdermilk, D. L., Jensen, M. D., & Perry, S. E. (1995), p. 125.

Reeder, S. J., Martin, L. L., & Koniak-Griffin, D. (1997), pp. 398-401.

7

8. correct answer: 2

1. This is a very good suggestion but it only partially meets the client's needs.

2. **During pregnancy, anemia results from an insufficient iron reserve, which leads to decreased hemoglobin and hematocrit levels. Iron intake must match the body's needs.**

3. A leave of absence from work may be effective in the short term but not sufficient to give the client the energy she needs during her pregnancy.

4. Sharing chores with her spouse will be beneficial in the short and long term but is only part of the solution. The spouse may already be doing his share of the household chores.

Classification

Competency Category:	Curative/Supportive Care
Taxonomic Level:	Critical Thinking
Client Type:	Individuals
Age Group:	Adult

References

Bobak, I. M., Lowdermilk, D. L., Jensen, M. D., & Perry, S. E. (1995), p. 147.

Reeder, S. J., Martin, L. L., & Koniak-Griffin, D. (1997), pp. 373-374.

9. correct answer: 3

1. Pregnancy aggravates venous congestion of the lower limbs; wearing support stockings reduces this congestion, but does not help avoid injuries.

2. This measure will reduce congestion of the lower limbs and ankle edema, but does not prevent falls.

3. **Wearing flat shoes helps stabilize the centre of gravity and prevent falls.**

4. Reducing physical activity is not a means of preventing injuries.

Classification

Competency Category:	Illness/Injury Prevention
Taxonomic Level:	Knowledge/Comprehension
Client Type:	Individuals
Age Group:	Adult

References

Bobak, I. M., Lowdermilk, D. L., Jensen, M. D., & Perry, S. E. (1995), p. 141.

Reeder, S. J., Martin, L. L., & Koniak-Griffin, D. (1997), p. 420.

10. correct answer: 4

1. Placing the feet in dorsiflexion to stretch the muscles relieves leg cramps but not lower back pain.

2. Good posture when sitting or standing relieves dyspnea caused by the pressure of the gravid uterus on the diaphragm, but does not relieve back pain.

3. Avoiding crossing legs prevents venous congestion of the lower limbs but does not relieve back pain.

4. **A pelvic tilt relieves backache, while toning the abdominal muscles.**

Classification

Competency Category:	Curative/Supportive Care
Taxonomic Level:	Knowledge/Comprehension
Client Type:	Individuals
Age Group:	Adult

References

Bobak, I. M., Lowdermilk, D. L., Jensen, M. D., & Perry, S. E. (1995), p. 155.

Reeder, S. J., Martin, L. L., & Koniak-Griffin, D. (1997), p. 428.

11. correct answer: 3

1. Reducing the quantity of fluid consumed can reduce urinary frequency but other ailments, such as constipation, could occur.

2. Reducing fluids increases intestinal sluggishness, which is already being altered by the concentration of progesterone.

3. **Reducing fluid intake in the evenings will reduce night-time urinary output and promote sleep.**

4. This intervention does not provide the client with a solution.

Classification

Competency Category:	Curative/Supportive Care
Taxonomic Level:	Knowledge/Comprehension
Client Type:	Individuals
Age Group:	Adult

References

Bobak, I. M., Lowdermilk, D. L., Jensen, M. D., & Perry, S. E. (1995), p. 162.

Reeder, S. J., Martin, L. L., & Koniak-Griffin, D. (1997), p. 368.

7

12. correct answer: 4

1. Exercise is excellent and helps prevent constipation, but it must also be accompanied by a high-fibre diet.

2. The iron supplement is necessary for a pregnant woman to maintain normal hemoglobin and hematocrit levels and for the fetus to store iron in the third trimester.

3. A pregnant woman must have a physician's prescription for medication to relieve constipation.

4. **The measures to prevent constipation consist of drinking sufficient fluids (fluid intake of at least two litres a day) and ensuring a high-fibre diet.**

Classification

Competency Category:	Curative/Supportive Care
Taxonomic Level:	Knowledge/Comprehension
Client Type:	Individuals
Age Group:	Adult

References

Lowdermilk, D. L., Perry, S. E., & Bobak, I. M. (1997), p. 237.

Reeder, S. J., Martin, L. L., & Koniak-Griffin, D. (1997), p. 427.

13. correct answer: 3

1. A survey only helps in obtaining certain data and does not promote intersectoral cooperation for the purpose of health promotion.

2. It is too early in the process to facilitate a support group.

3. **This initiative is the first step toward the intersectoral cooperation process designed to raise awareness about the issue among people in the school and community.**

4. Consulting co-workers is part of intradisciplinary cooperation and does not guarantee that a project will be introduced.

Classification

Competency Category:	Health Promotion
Taxonomic Level:	Application
Client Type:	Groups, Populations, Communities
Age Group:	Child & Adolescent

References

Canadian Nurses Association. (1997), *Code of Ethics for Registered Nurses,* p. 9.

Hitchcock, J. E., & Thomas, S. A. (1999), p. 322.

14. correct answer: 4

1. Sharing her fears might undermine the establishment of an effective relationship with the students.

2. Although this is an important step, it does not show sensitivity to the students' choices and needs.

3. This measure does not necessarily show respect for the students' values and behaviours.

4. **This is an essential attitude that must accompany any action taken by the nurse to induce the students to analyze their values, choices and decisions.**

Classification

Competency Category:	Nurse-Client Relationship
Taxonomic Level:	Affective
Client Type:	Groups, Populations, Communities
Age Group:	Child & Adolescent

References

Canadian Nurses Association. (1997), *Code of Ethics for Registered Nurses,* p. 13.

Wong, D. L. (1995), pp. 920-921.

15. correct answer: 4

1. This approach respects the confidentiality aspect of the nurse's role, but runs counter to the nurse's professional responsibilities.

2. This approach runs counter to respecting the confidentiality of what the nurse has been told.

3. The nurse could adopt this approach if she obtains Sarah's consent or if she deems that Sarah's behaviour is endangering her life.

4. **Guide Julie to realize that she is telling the nurse about this matter so Sarah can obtain help. Guide her to clarify her values in this respect.**

Classification

Competency Category:	Professional Practice
Taxonomic Level:	Knowledge/Comprehension
Client Type:	Groups, Populations, Communities
Age Group:	Child & Adolescent

References

Canadian Nurses Association. (1997), *Code of Ethics for Registered Nurses,* pp. 15-16.

Wong, D. L. (1995), p. 921.

Smith, C. M., & Maurer, F. A. (1995), pp. 101-102.

7

16. correct answer: 4

1. The fact that she wants to handle this situation by herself is not evidence that the client is managing her own health.

2. Friends are not always a dependable resource. The client adopts a passive attitude in accepting help from her friends.

3. The physician may be a support but there is no indication that the client will take measures to manage her health.

4. **Participation in a support group is evidence that the client is undergoing a process of self-empowerment.**

Classification

Competency Category:	Health Promotion
Taxonomic Level:	Application
Client Type:	Groups, Populations, Communities
Age Group:	Child & Adolescent

References

Hitchcock, J. E., & Thomas, S. A. (1999), p. 635.

Wong, D. L. (1995), p. 921.

17. correct answer: 1

1. **Identifying sources of stress and managing them effectively help prevent relapses.**

2. With drug abuse, attempts must be made to reduce social isolation.

3. Family activities are appropriate when they are coupled with appropriate support from family members.

4. An activity log is not sufficient to prevent relapses.

Classification

Competency Category:	Illness/Injury Prevention
Taxonomic Level:	Knowledge/Comprehension
Client Type:	Groups, Populations, Communities
Age Group:	Child & Adolescent

References

Boyd, M. A., & Nihart, M. A. (1998), pp. 757-760.

Wong, D. L. (1995), pp. 920-921.

18. correct answer: 4

1. Obstacle to communication. The nurse is belittling what the client is experiencing.

2. The nurse is not respecting the client's pace and is providing false reassurance.

3. The nurse is reassuring the client and is not taking his emotions into account.

4. **The nurse is validating the message received from the client and displaying empathy.**

Classification

Competency Category:	Nurse-Client Relationship
Taxonomic Level:	Affective
Client Type:	Individuals
Age Group:	Adult

References

Boyd, M. A., & Nihart, M. A. (1998), p. 254.

Varcarolis, E. M. (1998), p. 152.

19. correct answer: 2

1. Asking to see his wife is not related to the decision to commit suicide.

2. **The improved mood may result from his decision to act on his desires.**

3. Wishing to settle his financial problems is not directly linked to the decision to commit suicide.

4. Not wishing to join a support group does not reflect a suicide plan.

Classification

Competency Category:	Illness/Injury Prevention
Taxonomic Level:	Application
Client Type:	Individuals
Age Group:	Adult

References

Boyd, M. A., & Nihart, M. A. (1998), p. 449.

Varcarolis, E. M. (1998), p. 730.

20. correct answer: 4

1. Listening does not necessarily mean that the client has fully understood what the resource person has expressed about depression.

2. Explaining the experiences of people with depression distances the client from his own experience.

3. Leaving the group indicates that the client is going through a difficult experience and is not ready to express himself freely in front of the group. The nurse's action does not respect the client's pace.

4. **Interacting with members of the group shows the client's interest in understanding what they are experiencing. By sharing his own experience, he is demonstrating his commitment.**

Classification

Competency Category:	Nurse-Client Relationship
Taxonomic Level:	Application
Client Type:	Groups, Populations, Communities
Age Group:	Adult

References

Boyd, M. A., & Nihart, M. A. (1998), p. 322.

Varcarolis, E. M. (1998), p. 730.

7

21. correct answer: 3

1. Having him return to his room could be a therapeutic action if it is not coupled with a punitive measure.

2. He is angry and his capacity for reasoning is diminished.

3. **Offering him this choice allows him to regain self-control and to be listened to by a person whom he trusts.**

4. The presence of security guards and the application of physical restraints at this stage could increase his level of anxiety and undermine the relationship of trust.

Classification

Competency Category:	Illness/Injury Prevention
Taxonomic Level:	Application
Client Type:	Individuals
Age Group:	Adult

References

Boyd, M. A., & Nihart, M. A. (1998), p. 1040.

Varcarolis, E. M. (1998), p. 312.

22. correct answer: 2

1. Confronting the client is not appropriate at this stage and displays a lack of understanding and respect for the self-concept adaptation process.

2. **This measure allows the person to use sound and effective adaptation strategies and to acquire positive feelings about himself.**

3. The client decides on his treatment plan and any other approaches designed to improve his health condition.

4. When the client presents a dissociative identity disorder, the nurse must respect the client's pace of expression and not pressure him to interact with more than one person at a time.

Classification

Competency Category:	Nurse-Client Relationship
Taxonomic Level:	Application
Client Type:	Individuals
Age Group:	Adult

References

Haber, J., Krainovich-Miller, B., McMahon, A. L., & Price-Hoskins, P. (1997), p. 422.

Boyd, M. A., & Nihart, M. A. (1998), p. 254.

Varcarolis, E. M. (1998), pp. 312-313.

23. correct answer: 2

1. Clients who present a potential for suicide are placed near the nursing station, and usually in the presence of another client, to enable closer observation and to prevent destructive actions.

2. **At this stage, it is vital to protect the client, to prevent any attempt at self-destruction.**

3. Before administering medication, it is important to remove the client's personal effects to reduce the risk of injury.

4. The family is not responsible for supervising the client.

Classification

Competency Category:	Illness/Injury Prevention
Taxonomic Level:	Application
Client Type:	Individuals
Age Group:	Adult

References

Boyd, M. A., & Nihart, M. A. (1998), p. 138.
Carpentino, L. J. (1995), p. 181.

24. correct answer: 4

1. Iodized contrast media is not injected into the bowel during a colonoscopy.

2. A radiopaque catheter is not introduced into the bowel during a colonoscopy.

3. The instrument used during a colonoscopy is a fibroscope, not a rectal tube.

4. **The use of a flexible fibroscope allows examination of the large bowel mucosa and helps to localize the source of bleeding in the lower gastrointestinal tract.**

Classification

Competency Category:	Curative/Supportive Care
Taxonomic Level:	Knowledge/Comprehension
Client Type:	Individuals
Age Group:	Child & Adolescent

References

Smeltzer, S. C., & Bare, B. G. (1996), p. 827.
Nettina, S. M. (1996), pp. 484-486.

25. correct answer: 2

1. Weight loss is a common problem in inflammatory bowel disease but this data is not a priority.

2. **The care objective is to determine the relationship between the diarrheal stools and food intake, activity and/or emotional stress.**

3. Assessment of the effect on lifestyle of the chronic pain of an inflammatory bowel process is not priority data during admission of a client in the acute phase.

4. This is an important piece of information that indicates hydroelectrolytic imbalance and malnutrition, but it is not a priority in this situation.

Classification

Competency Category:	Curative/Supportive Care
Taxonomic Level:	Critical Thinking
Client Type:	Individuals
Age Group:	Child & Adolescent

References

Smeltzer, S. C., & Bare, B. G. (1996), p. 926.

Nettina, S. M. (1996), p. 526.

26. correct answer: 3

1. This diet is ordered to meet the client's nutritional needs, not to reduce oral pain.

2. This diet allows the bowel to rest and is not necessarily associated with weight gain or weight loss.

3. **A fibre-restricted diet containing protein concentrates reduces intestinal activity and pain and improves protein repletion.**

4. This type of diet does not replace electrolytes and fluid lost during episodes of diarrhea.

Classification

Competency Category:	Curative/Supportive Care
Taxonomic Level:	Critical Thinking
Client Type:	Individuals
Age Group:	Child & Adolescent

References

Smeltzer, S. C., & Bare, B. G. (1996), p. 926.

Nettina, S. M. (1996), p. 526.

27. correct answer: 2

1. Salazopyrin will decrease the rapid propulsion of fecal matter through the bowel and consequently increase electrolytic absorption. However, it is not used as an electrolytic replacement.

2. **Salazopyrin has an anti-inflammatory effect on the intestinal mucosa. Since the colon is no longer inflamed, it will be able to re-absorb fluid and electrolytes and consequently, the diarrhea will diminish.**

3. Salazopyrin rarely causes insomnia.

4. Treatment with salazopyrin can cause hemolysis which results in anemia.

Classification

Competency Category:	Curative/Supportive Care
Taxonomic Level:	Knowledge/Comprehension
Client Type:	Individuals
Age Group:	Child & Adolescent

References

Smeltzer, S. C., & Bare, B. G. (1996), p. 924.
Nettina, S. M. (1996), p. 525.

28. correct answer: 1

1. **This strategy is a priority in the demystification of inflammatory bowel disease; for example, somatization.**

2. Clients with inflammatory bowel disease often sense they are losing control over various aspects of their lives. It is preferable to allow these clients some self-management of their care.

3. This consultation will not be necessary unless the client behaviour indicates that she cannot cope. The nurse can reserve some time each day to help the client develop coping strategies.

4. The nurse is assuming that the client has a need to manage her stress. It is preferable to reinforce effective coping strategies and involve family members in the care.

Classification

Competency Category:	Illness/Injury Prevention
Taxonomic Level:	Knowledge/Comprehension
Client Type:	Individuals
Age Group:	Child & Adolescent

References

Smeltzer, S. C., & Bare, B. G. (1996), p. 927.
Nettina, S. M. (1996), p. 527.

7

29. correct answer: 3

1. Knowledge of community resources might encourage the client to participate in support groups, but it is not sufficient in itself.

2. This service does not address her current needs.

3. **By learning about the therapeutic effects of the support group, the client will be more interested in participating.**

4. This measure can increase the client's level of knowledge about her illness, but it does not promote sharing experiences.

Classification

Competency Category:	Health Promotion
Taxonomic Level:	Application
Client Type:	Individuals
Age Group:	Child & Adolescent

References

Haber, J., Krainovich-Miller, B., McMahon, A. L., & Price-Hoskins, P. (1997), pp. 710-711.

Nettina, S. M. (1996), p. 527.

30. correct answer: 2

1. The family's relationships with health professionals may accentuate or alleviate the stress caused by a health problem. There is no indication that the relationships are a problem.

2. **The client has disturbed sleep habits that are creating health problems and changes in activities of daily living for his wife and main caregiver.**

3. Communication between the family members is not a priority in this situation.

4. It can be assumed that the time and energy required for certain care restricts social activities, but there is no indication that isolation is observed in this situation.

Classification

Competency Category:	Curative/Supportive Care
Taxonomic Level:	Application
Client Type:	Families
Age Group:	Adult of Advanced Age

References

Matteson, M. A., McConnell, E. S., & Linton, A. D. (1997), p. 13.

Luecknotte, A. G. (1996), pp. 376-377.

31. correct answer: 2

1. The client's wife will become aware of her support network: children, friends, neighbours or community services. This action should take place after her consent is obtained.

2. **The client's wife will be encouraged to verbalize her feelings about her problems. Subsequently, she will realize that she needs outside help.**

3. The client's wife is the main caregiver in this situation. Night roaming often requires intervention to reduce risks inside the home, and day or night sitter services to allow the client's wife to rest.

4. This intervention does not consider the wife's multiple responsibilities in caring for her husband, and provides no solution.

Classification

Competency Category:	Curative/Supportive Care
Taxonomic Level:	Critical Thinking
Client Type:	Families
Age Group:	Adult of Advanced Age

References

Matteson, M. A., McConnell, E. S., & Linton, A. D. (1997), p. 685.

Luecknotte, A. G. (1996), pp. 376-377.

32. correct answer: 2

1. Using an alarm bell will not prevent falls; it will warn the wife that her husband is leaving the bedroom.

2. **In the case of a client who roams at night, the house should have adequate lighting to eliminate the risk of falls.**

3. Sleeping medication is not recommended because it increases the risk of falls.

4. This suggestion is not always realistic and is very costly.

Classification

Competency Category:	Illness/Injury Prevention
Taxonomic Level:	Knowledge/Comprehension
Client Type:	Families
Age Group:	Adult of Advanced Age

References

Matteson, M. A., McConnell, E. S., & Linton, A. D. (1997), p. 685.

Haber, J., Krainovich-Miller, B., McMahon, A. L., & Price-Hoskins, P. (1997), p. 676.

33. correct answer: 3

1. Rather than reinforcing the wife's sense of control, this response may provoke emotional distress.

2. This response does not encourage the wife's participation in the decisions.

3. **This option helps the wife to become aware of her ability to gain control and to continue in her role of caregiver.**

4. The nurse is not considering the wife's feelings.

Classification

Competency Category:	Curative/Supportive Care
Taxonomic Level:	Application
Client Type:	Families
Age Group:	Adult of Advanced Age

References

Matteson, M. A., McConnell, E. S., & Linton, A. D. (1997), p. 919.

Haber, J., Krainovich-Miller, B., McMahon, A. L., & Price-Hoskins, P. (1997), p. 681.

34. correct answer: 1

1. **The nurse respects the wife's wishes and helps her to consider all aspects of her decision.**

2. It is premature to seek help before taking steps with the wife.

3. This action is pointless and does not reflect advocacy for the wife.

4. The nurse is not acting as an advocate for the wife.

Classification

Competency Category:	Professional Practice
Taxonomic Level:	Application
Client Type:	Families
Age Group:	Adult of Advanced Age

References

Matteson, M. A., McConnell, E. S., & Linton, A. D. (1997), pp. 918-920.

Canadian Nurses Association. (1997), *Code of Ethics for Registered Nurses*, pp. 10-11.

35. correct answer: 3

1. Although it remains controversial, mammograms should begin at the age of 40. The client's daughters are young adults.

2. A Pap test is recommended yearly for women of childbearing age. This test is not used to detect breast cancer.

3. **Cancer societies recommend that monthly breast self-exams by women over the age of 20 be a routine health habit.**

4. Pelvic exams should be done as the Pap test is done, on a yearly basis. This does not address the mother's concern with early breast cancer detection.

Classification

Competency Category:	Health Promotion
Taxonomic Level:	Application
Client Type:	Families
Age Group:	Adult

References

Phipps, W., Cassmeyer, V., Sands, J., & Lehman, M. (1995), p. 385.

Smeltzer, S. C., & Bare, B. G. (1996), pp. 1304-1305.

36. correct answer: 2

1. The client is experiencing postoperative urinary retention. Reducing the IV flow rate does not address the problem.

2. **Key assessments in monitoring for output complications are intake and output data and a distended bladder. Urinary retention is a common postoperative complication.**

3. This intervention is not a priority at this time. The client is exhibiting signs and symptoms of urinary retention. She needs to be assessed for urinary retention.

4. This is assessment data for infection. At the present time the nurse needs to assess the client for signs of urinary retention.

Classification

Competency Category:	Curative/Supportive Care
Taxonomic Level:	Application
Client Type:	Individuals
Age Group:	Adult

References

Potter, P. A., & Perry, A. G. (1999), p. 976.

Taylor, C., Lillis, C., & LeMone, P. (1997), p. 1256.

37. correct answer: 2

1. This response does not validate the client's feelings and sets up a barrier to communication. The client's feelings need to be acknowledged in a non-judgmental manner.

2. **This response validates the client's feelings and invites the client to share more of her concerns, feelings and fears. The nurse is acknowledging the client's concerns in a non-judgmental manner, which would promote further communication.**

3. This is false reassurance and negates the client's feelings, creating a barrier to further meaningful communication.

4. This response does not invite the client to share her feelings with the nurse. The client is providing the nurse with an opportunity to intervene in a therapeutic manner.

Classification

Competency Category:	Curative/Supportive Care
Taxonomic Level:	Application
Client Type:	Individuals
Age Group:	Adult

References

Potter, P. A., & Perry, A. G. (1999), pp. 401-403.

Taylor, C., Lillis, C., & LeMone, P. (1997), pp. 800-811.

38. correct answer: 3

1. The nurse's initial intervention should be to discuss the client's needs prior to contacting a spiritual adviser.

2. This may be appropriate, but the client's feelings of abandonment need to be addressed.

3. **This response is supportive to the client and allows the client to explore what has given meaning to her life.**

4. This response does not acknowledge the client's feelings. The nurse needs to explore with the client her feelings of spiritual abandonment and assist the client to resolve her spiritual distress.

Classification

Competency Category:	Curative/Supportive Care
Taxonomic Level:	Knowledge/Comprehension
Client Type:	Individuals
Age Group:	Adult

References

Potter, P. A., & Perry, A. G. (1999), pp. 294-296.

Taylor, C., Lillis, C., & LeMone, P. (1997), pp. 894-900.

39. correct answer: 1

1. **Post-mastectomy exercise promotes collateral circulation which prevents the development of lymphedema, a common post-mastectomy complication.**

2. Exercise can reduce the development of lymphedema in the postoperative and recovery phase. Its purpose is not to control pain.

3. Scarring at the operative site is not reduced by post-mastectomy arm exercises.

4. Exercise promotes venous lymphatic drainage.

Classification

Competency Category:	Rehabilitative Care
Taxonomic Level:	Knowledge/Comprehension
Client Type:	Individuals
Age Group:	Adult

References

Phipps, W., Cassmeyer, V., Sands, J., & Lehman, M. (1995), p. 1840.
Smeltzer, S. C., & Bare, B. G. (1996), p. 1324.

40. correct answer: 2

1. Gloves cannot be used for more than one client.

2. **Long fingernails and rings may cause tears in the gloves and increase the risk of contamination.**

3. Body substance precautions necessitate the use of gloves for any contact with body substances. All clients are considered potentially infective.

4. Wearing gloves is not a substitute for handwashing. Handwashing before and after client care will also reduce the incidence of nosocomial infections.

Classification

Competency Category:	Curative/Supportive Care
Taxonomic Level:	Knowledge/Comprehension
Client Type:	Individuals
Age Group:	Adult

References

Potter, P. A., & Perry, A. G. (1999), p. 570.
Taylor, C., Lillis, C., & LeMone, P (1997), pp. 570-576.

7

41. correct answer: 3

1. The client is presently confused, so answering yes or no to questions will not necessarily yield accurate information. In this situation, the best source of information is the client's family.

2. The client's health records could be used later to complete the information. In this situation, the best source of information is the client's family.

3. **Collecting data from family would be most reliable and constitute an immediate source of information.**

4. The client's condition is unstable and obtaining his health history is a priority at this time.

Classification

Competency Category:	Curative/Supportive Care
Taxonomic Level:	Knowledge/Comprehension
Client Type:	Families
Age Group:	Older Adult

References

Taylor, C., Lillis, C., & LeMone, P. (1997), p. 254.

Craven, R. F., & Hirnle, C. (1996), p. 160.

42. correct answer: 2

1. This data is not related to the effectiveness of the nitroglycerin infusion.

2. **The blood pressure should be assessed as the effects of this drug are seen in 2-5 minutes.**

3. This would not be an indicator of the effectiveness of the nitroglycerin infusion; headaches are a side effect of nitroglycerin.

4. This data is not related to the effectiveness of the nitroglycerin infusion.

Classification

Competency Category:	Illness/Injury Prevention
Taxonomic Level:	Application
Client Type:	Individuals
Age Group:	Older Adult

References

Williams, B. R., & Baer, C. L. (1998), p. 251.

Deglin, J. H., & Vallerand, A. H. (1997), p. 869.

43. correct answer: 3

1. Providing oxygen without assessing the patency of his airway is premature.

2. Assessing the patency of the client's airway is the priority. Placing the client in high Fowler's position is contraindicated in this situation.

3. **Airway maintenance is the priority. In anticipation of the need to initiate emergency measures, the nurse should recognize the need for assistance. This is basic protocol to be used when someone is found unresponsive.**

4. Never insert an oral airway without checking the patency of the client's airway. Again CPR protocols should be observed.

Classification

Competency Category:	Curative/Supportive Care
Taxonomic Level:	Application
Client Type:	Individuals
Age Group:	Older Adult

References

Craven, R. F., & Hirnle, C. (1996), p. 971.

Burton, G. G., Hodgkin, J. E., & Ward, J. J. (1997), p. 564.

44. correct answer: 3

1. Given the seriousness of the client's condition and weight, this method would be an unsafe method of transfer for the client and staff.

2. This is an inappropriate method of transfer for a client with left-sided weakness. The client requires assistance while transferring to the stretcher.

3. **This intervention would assist the client to transfer safely to the stretcher, and prevent any injury to the nurse.**

4. It would be unsafe for the nurse to transfer the client by herself. The nurse needs to ask for assistance to prevent injury to the client and herself.

Classification

Competency Category:	Illness/Injury Prevention
Taxonomic Level:	Knowledge/Comprehension
Client Type:	Individuals
Age Group:	Older Adult

References

Taylor, C., Lillis, C., & LeMone, P. (1997), p. 1049.

Craven, R. F., & Hirnle, C. (1996), p. 857.

7

45. correct answer: 2

1. This response is not showing empathy for the client but rather telling him what he "should" be able to do.

2. **This response demonstrates empathy, provides him some positive feedback, and allows the client to explore his concerns.**

3. This response does not allow the nurse to explore the client's concerns and offers a solution that may not be appropriate.

4. This response is patronizing and does not address the client's concerns.

Classification

Competency Category:	Rehabilitative Care
Taxonomic Level:	Application
Client Type:	Individuals
Age Group:	Older Adult

References

Craven, R. F., & Hirnle, C. (1996), pp. 353-355.

Riley, J. W., Balzer. (1996), p. 177.

46. correct answer: 3

1. This option does not give the client any group support, which is known to be very effective in successful weight loss.

2. This also does not involve the client in any group/peer support activities, which have been proven to be supportive and beneficial in weight loss programs.

3. **Self-help groups are recognized as more beneficial than individual help. Sharing experiences and mutual understanding can be very motivating in weight loss programs.**

4. This is an appropriate intervention, but it is not the most effective in encouraging the client to comply with the low calorie diet.

Classification

Competency Category:	Health Promotion
Taxonomic Level:	Application
Client Type:	Individuals
Age Group:	Older Adult

References

Dudek, S. G. (1997), p. 397.

Drummond, K. E. (1994), p. 283.

47. correct answer: 4

1. The nurse has made recommendations without completing an assessment.
2. Although this may be true, this does not address the client's concern.
3. This is likely to be necessary but the nurse has ignored the daughter's statement about her father's attitude toward doctors.
4. **The nurse can complete her assessment with the daughter present to support her father and to help plan a course of follow-up if needed.**

Classification

Competency Category:	Curative/Supportive Care
Taxonomic Level:	Application
Client Type:	Families
Age Group:	Older Adult

References

Matteson, M. A., McConnell, E. S., & Linton, A. D. (1997), p. 532.

Johnson, J. Y., Smith-Temple, J., & Carr, P. (1998), p. 23.

48. correct answer: 1

1. **The client's physiological response should influence the course of action. The nurse should communicate these findings to the surgeon when the hemoglobin is reported.**
2. It is not within the nurse's scope of practice to initiate this action without a doctor's order.
3. This is premature without further assessment data.
4. This should be done after assessing the client for symptoms of low hemoglobin.

Classification

Competency Category:	Curative/Supportive Care
Taxonomic Level:	Knowledge/Comprehension
Client Type:	Individuals
Age Group:	Older Adult

References

Phipps, W., Cassmeyer, V., Sands, J., & Lehman, M. (1995), pp. 1789-1796.

Harkness, G. A., & Dincher, J. R. (1996), p. 872.

49. correct answer: 4

1. This response does not acknowledge the client's feelings at this time.

2. This intervention may be appropriate, but does not address the client's concerns.

3. The client is expressing to the nurse his need to be with his pet. This intervention does not address his concern.

4. The nurse acknowledges the client's feelings and needs. She also recognizes the benefits that having the client's pet visit him in hospital may have on his recovery.

Classification

Competency Category: Health Promotion
Taxonomic Level: Knowledge/Comprehension
Client Type: Individuals
Age Group: Older Adult

References

Hogstel, M. O. (1995), p. 39.
Eliopoulos, C. (1997), p. 27.

50. correct answer: 4

1. The nurse is avoiding the question and perhaps needs to examine her level of comfort in discussions of sexuality.

2. The question is being deferred to the surgeon and the nurse is ignoring the fact that he directed the question to her, perhaps because "he isn't fond of doctors."

3. The nurse is assuming a knowledge deficit but this will not help to explore issues of self-esteem, or changes in body image.

4. The nurse is responsive to the client's feelings and asks an open-ended question to facilitate communication.

Classification

Competency Category: Health Promotion
Taxonomic Level: Knowledge/Comprehension
Client Type: Individuals
Age Group: Older Adult

References

Ebersole, P., & Hess, P. (1998), p. 587.
Van Servellen, G. M. (1997), p. 113.

51. correct answer: 3

1. This information prompts the referral to the community care nurse but they may not necessarily follow up with a home visit.

2. The unusual location is information the community care nurse would appreciate.

3. **This information relays an immediacy to the community care nurse to follow up with a home visit.**

4. This is additional information the nurse should include.

Classification

Competency Category:	Curative/Supportive Care
Taxonomic Level:	Application
Client Type:	Families
Age Group:	Older Adult

References

Clemen-Stone, S., Eigsti, D. G., & McGuire, S. L. (1995), p. 349.
Hitchcock, J. E ., & Thomas, S. A. (1999), p. 343.

52. correct answer: 3

1. Incorrect because it demonstrates a lack of understanding about how AZT works in the body.

2. Incorrect because it demonstrates a lack of understanding about how AZT works in the body.

3. **This demonstrates an understanding of how AZT works. The client has an opportunistic disease, which is the most common condition to affect people with HIV.**

4. Incorrect because it demonstrates a lack of understanding about how AZT works in the body.

Classification

Competency Category:	Health Promotion
Taxonomic Level:	Critical Thinking
Client Type:	Individuals
Age Group:	Adult

References

Rosdahl, C. B. (1995), p. 1173.
Ignatavicius, D. D., Workman, M. L., & Mishler, M. A. (1995), p. 505.

7

53. correct answer: 1

1. The client's immune system is compromised. He is currently suffering from an opportunistic infection. The lesions made by tattooing would increase the likelihood of infection.

2. Although this choice acknowledges how he is feeling, it does not address the danger to the client of getting a tattoo.

3. The nurse needs to inform the client of the risks of this procedure in relation to his compromised immune system.

4. Although nurses should give this warning to people who indicate that they wish to have tattoos, it does not consider the client's current state of compromised health.

Classification

Competency Category:	Illness/Injury Prevention
Taxonomic Level:	Critical Thinking
Client Type:	Families
Age Group:	Adult

References

Ignatavicius, D. D., Workman, M. L., & Mishler, M. A. (1995), p. 519.

Ferris, F. D., & Cummings, I. (1995), p. 84.

54. correct answer: 3

1. This minimizes the client's feelings and is patronizing. This communicates that the client does not have permission to discuss his thoughts about dying.

2. It is outside the nurse's scope of practice to approve a client's request to not be resuscitated.

3. It is important to ensure that the client clearly understands the distinction between a no CPR and a "Do Not Resuscitate" (DNR) request. This will enable the client to make an informed choice based on facts.

4. This response minimizes the client's feelings and may also be considered to be false hope.

Classification

Competency Category:	Professional Practice
Taxonomic Level:	Critical Thinking
Client Type:	Individuals
Age Group:	Adult

References

Keatings, M., & Smith, O. (2000), pp. 268-270.

Ferris, F. D., & Cummings, I. (1995), p. 127.

Grant, A. E., & Ashman, A. A. (1997), p. 172.

55. correct answer: 4

1. Although it is true that the client needs to be isolated from other people when he is compromised, this strategy does nothing to address the client's feelings of loneliness.

2. Although it is true that some people avoid patients with HIV because of fear, this is an inappropriate response and does not address the client's feelings of loneliness.

3. The nurse should first determine if family members are available and supportive. Also, the nurse should be responsible for providing supportive care.

4. **The nurse can help ease the feelings of isolation by organizing her workload to include supportive care to the client.**

Classification

Competency Category:	Curative/Supportive Care
Taxonomic Level:	Application
Client Type:	Individuals
Age Group:	Adult

References

Ferris, F. D., & Cummings, I. (1995), p. 101.

Doenges, M. E. (1997), p. 760.

56. correct answer: 4

1. A mask would be worn in this scenario to protect the client from infection, not to protect the nurses.

2. A gown is only necessary during contact with secretions/excretions, not each time the nurse enters the client's room.

3. The research demonstrates that there is no danger of contracting HIV from utensils such as these.

4. **This is one of the most important measures that a nurse can use to prevent occupational exposure to any infection.**

Classification

Competency Category:	Illness/Injury Prevention
Taxonomic Level:	Application
Client Type:	Individuals
Age Group:	Adult

References

Ferris, F. D., & Cummings, I. (1995), p. 152.

Doenges, M. E. (1997), p. 744.

7

57. correct answer: 3

1. The client's anxiety about the potential for skin breakdown is legitimate. A referral to a psychologist is not warranted.

2. The suggestion is not research-based and could result in harm to the client.

3. **The social worker helps clients identify and access support services and resources, including investigating potential financial resources. The client would benefit as much from an air bed at home as he has in hospital.**

4. This intervention does not address the underlying issue of the client's financial resources.

Classification

Competency Category: Nurse-Client Relationship
Taxonomic Level: Knowledge/Comprehension
Client Type: Individuals
Age Group: Adult

References

Ignatavicius, D. D., Workman, M. L., & Mishler, M. A. (1995), p. 219.

Ferris, F. D., & Cummings, I. (1995), p. 100.

58. correct answer: 4

1. The nurse greets the client but pays no attention to the client's non-verbal communication. Use of the first name could be intrusive.

2. The nurse greets the client using her first name only, which could be intrusive. However, she introduces herself, which can facilitate establishment of a relationship with the client. Although the nurse realizes that something is not right, she proposes a solution instead of listening.

3. The nurse greets the client but does not introduce herself. She is sensitive to non-verbal language, but intervenes by asking a closed question; this does not facilitate communication.

4. **Communication is facilitated by greeting the client by her name and introducing oneself. The nurse shows that she is sensitive to the client's non-verbal message by sharing her observations with her.**

Classification

Competency Category: Nurse-Client Relationship
Taxonomic Level: Knowledge/Comprehension
Client Type: Individuals
Age Group: Adult of Advanced Age

References

Taylor, C., Lillis, C., & LeMone, P. (1997), pp. 366, 369.

DuGas, B. W., & Knor, E. R. (1995), p. 403.

59. correct answer: 4

1. It is preferable to let the adolescent establish her own schedule of activities and manage her time appropriately.

2. Reflection is sometimes more appropriate than punishment.

3. It is preferable to teach her how to make decisions.

4. **This method helps her acquire a sense of responsibility.**

Classification

Competency Category:	Nurse-Client Relationship
Taxonomic Level:	Application
Client Type:	Families
Age Group:	Child & Adolescent.

References

Hitchcock, J. E., & Thomas, S. A. (1999), p. 378.

Wong, D. L. (1995), pp. 194-195, 965-966.

60. correct answer: 4

1. The statement is incomplete; a healthy lifestyle must involve all aspects of a person.

2. This statement is incomplete. The bio-physiological, cognitive, cultural and environmental dimensions are missing.

3. This point focuses more on the concept of protecting health and is not exclusive to contagious diseases.

4. **Health promotion strategies influence a person's well-being.**

Classification

Competency Category:	Health Promotion
Taxonomic Level:	Application
Client Type:	Groups, Populations, Communities
Age Group:	Child & Adolescent

References

Hunt, R., & Zurek, E. (1997), pp. 63-67.

Cookfair, J. M. (1996), pp. 147-149.

7

61. correct answer: 2

1. The fact that the nurse gives the client some leaflets does not mean that he will take the time to read them and that he will understand the content.

2. **Using this strategy, the nurse can assess the client's understanding, reply to his questions, and involve his wife.**

3. The client's learning needs are not met by giving him a research article. He is likely to interpret the content in his own way.

4. A support group is formed for people who have experienced the same health problem. In this case, it would be appropriate for the questions to come from the client.

Classification

Competency Category:	Health Promotion
Taxonomic Level:	Application
Client Type:	Families
Age Group:	Older Adult

References

Hunt, R., & Zurek, E. (1997), p. 187.

Cookfair, J. M. (1996), p. 185.

62. correct answer: 2

1. The ability to learn depends on a person's physical and cognitive characteristics and is important, but the client must be motivated to learn.

2. **Numerous variables can influence the client's behaviour and learning situation. The most important is readiness to learn.**

3. Life experience is closely linked to the emotional aspect of readiness to learn.

4. The nurse must create a pleasant and warm atmosphere and show empathy; this will reinforce readiness to learn.

Classification

Competency Category:	Health Promotion
Taxonomic Level:	Application
Client Type:	Individuals
Age Group:	Not Applicable

References

Hitchcock, J. E., Schubert, P. E., & Thomas, S. A. (1999), pp. 108-110.

Smeltzer, S. C., & Bare, B. G. (1996), p. 41.

63. correct answer: 3

1. Everyone is at risk to develop an alcohol problem.
2. Many people grow up in an environment in which there is an alcohol problem, but never develop an alcohol-abuse problem.
3. **Sociocultural studies establish a link between sociocultural attitudes and alcohol abuse.**
4. The link between alcohol abuse and personality disorders has not been demonstrated scientifically.

Classification

Competency Category:	Health Promotion
Taxonomic Level:	Knowledge/Comprehension
Client Type:	Families
Age Group:	Child & Adolescent

References

Hitchcock, J. E., Schubert, P. E., & Thomas, S. A. (1999), pp. 614-615.
Boyd, M. A., & Nihart, M. A. (1998), p. 717.

64. correct answer: 3

1. Adopting safety measures does not increase the activity level.
2. Appropriate body alignment does not increase the activity level.
3. **Performing the range-of-motion exercises leads people to be more active and prepares them more effectively for walking.**
4. Raising the feet does not necessarily encourage activity.

Classification

Competency Category:	Health Promotion
Taxonomic Level:	Application
Client Type:	Groups, Populations, Communities
Age Group:	Older Adult

References

Hitchcock, J. E., Schubert, P. E., & Thomas, S. A. (1999), pp. 298-299.
Carpentino, L. J. (1995), p. 636.

65. correct answer: 4

1. Providing condoms does not ensure that they are used.
2. Encouraging abstinence does not ensure adoption of safe sexual practices.
3. Teaching pregnancy prevention methods does not ensure adoption of safe sexual practices.
4. **The teaching of safe-sex practices includes methods for preventing pregnancy and sexually transmitted diseases.**

Classification

Competency Category:	Health Promotion
Taxonomic Level:	Knowledge/Comprehension
Client Type:	Groups, Populations, Communities
Age Group:	Child & Adolescent

References

Hitchcock, J. E., Schubert, P. E., & Thomas, S. A. (1999), pp. 374-375.
Taylor, C., Lillis, C., & LeMone, P. (1997), p. 148.

7

66. correct answer: 3

1. There is no indication in this case that the client has a sedentary lifestyle and that he experiences considerable stress.

2. Tachycardia is a manifestation rather than a risk factor.

3. **Excess weight increases the work of the heart and increases the predisposition to myocardial infarction. Smoking hinders transportation of oxygen to the heart muscle and increases the demand for oxygen.**

4. A myocardial infarction usually occurs in adults. Drinking 120 ml of rye a week is not considered a risk factor.

Classification

Competency Category:	Illness/Injury Prevention
Taxonomic Level:	Critical Thinking
Client Type:	Individuals
Age Group:	Adult

References

Smeltzer, S. C., & Bare, B. G. (1996), p. 597.

Phipps, W. J., Cassmeyer, V. L., Sands, J. K., & Lehman, M. K. (1995), pp. 828-829.

67. correct answer: 3

1. Wearing a mask is only required when there is a risk of body fluid splashes.

2. Wearing a gown is only required when there is a risk of contamination by body fluids.

3. **Wearing gloves is essential to prevent contamination during handling of body fluids.**

4. Wearing glasses is only required when there is a risk of splashes and is necessary with all body fluids.

Classification

Competency Category:	Illness/Injury Prevention
Taxonomic Level:	Knowledge/Comprehension
Client Type:	Individuals
Age Group:	Adult

References

Phipps, W. J., Cassmeyer, V. L., Sands, J. K., & Lehman, M. K. (1995), p. 2443.

Taylor, C., Lillis, C., & LeMone, P. (1997), p. 577.

68. correct answer: 2

1. This approach could cause guilt feelings.

2. **This approach raises his awareness about his real needs and promotes self-empowerment.**

3. It is preferable to continue with the existing approach while re-assessing the needs related to his lifestyle.

4. This decision must be made jointly with the client; it is up to him to take the initiative.

Classification

Competency Category:	Illness/Injury Prevention
Taxonomic Level:	Application
Client Type:	Individuals
Age Group:	Older Adult

References

Hitchcock, J. E., Schubert, P. E., & Thomas, S. A. (1999), pp. 518, 534.
Nettina, S. (1996), pp. 288-292.

69. correct answer: 1

1. **Sudden changes in natremia affect re-absorption of Lithium by the kidneys, hence the importance of maintaining a certain balance in the absorption of salt and liquids.**

2. Because of Lithium's half-life of 24 hours, it is preferable not to take missed doses.

3. Lithemia must be assessed every six months, unless there are signs of toxicity.

4. The medication is usually taken indefinitely.

Classification

Competency Category:	Illness/Injury Prevention
Taxonomic Level:	Application
Client Type:	Individuals
Age Group:	Older Adult

References

Haber, J., Krainovich-Miller, B., McMahon, A. L., & Price-Hoskins, P. (1997), pp. 278, 279.
Boyd, M. A., & Nihart, M. A. (1998), p. 221.
Karch, A. M. (1999), pp. 695-696.

7

70. correct answer: 1

1. **When conducting a health evaluation, the nurse can gather all the necessary data and identify the changes in health.**

2. Since the nurse has an increasing amount of independence, she must first take into account the health evaluation, before consulting the dietician.

3. This method is not a reliable data collection tool for this client.

4. The screening test is an appropriate data collection technique. It becomes a measurement of the alcohol level in the blood, but it is not an independent nursing intervention.

Classification

Competency Category:	Curative/Supportive Care
Taxonomic Level:	Knowledge/Comprehension
Client Type:	Individuals
Age Group:	Adult

References

Haber, J., Krainovich-Miller, B., McMahon, A. L., & Price-Hoskins, P. (1997), pp. 525-526.

Boyd, M. A., & Nihart, M. A. (1998), pp. 744-745.

71. correct answer: 3

1. These are important data for overall health assessment, but not directly related to contracting HIV.

2. Alcohol and medication use is not directly related to contracting HIV. This affects the person's overall state of health.

3. **Sexual activity and intravenous drug use increase the person's risk of contracting HIV.**

4. The medical history is important but is not directly related to the person's current concern. It is too early to confirm the presence of HIV with blood tests.

Classification

Competency Category:	Curative/Supportive Care
Taxonomic Level:	Critical Thinking
Client Type:	Individuals
Age Group:	Child & Adolescent

References

Hitchcock, J. E., Schubert, P. E., & Thomas, S. A. (1999), pp. 374-375.

Carpentino, L. J. (1995), pp. 790, 821-822.

72. correct answer: 3

1. The client may easily be able to explain self–injection, but he has not demonstrated that he can do it. He must be able to demonstrate what he has learned.

2. Involvement and support of the client's wife is important, but the statement does not show that the client can practise the teaching received.

3. **One of the principles of teaching and learning is to observe the client demonstrating what he has learned, in order to assess learning.**

4. The fact that the client used the same medication before his hospitalization does not provide the nurse with any information about his ability to self–administer the medication.

Classification

Competency Category:	Curative/Supportive Care
Taxonomic Level:	Application
Client Type:	Individuals
Age Group:	Older Adult

References

Hitchcock, J. E., Schubert, P. E., & Thomas, S. A. (1997), p. 177.

Taylor, C., Lillis, C., & LeMone, P. (1997), p. 402.

73. correct answer: 2

1. Changing position reduces the risks of vascular and pulmonary complications, but must be done every two hours to facilitate optimal respiration.

2. **The vertical position facilitates movement of the diaphragm and increases thoracic disten-sion. Deep breathing results in more effective coughing.**

3. Fowler's position facilitates respiratory move-ment, but oxygen therapy is not necessary.

4. Administering an analgesic will alleviate the client's pain and thus might facilitate respiratory exercises. However, it does not ensure optimal ventilation and respiration. Having the client ambulate frequently facilitates optimal ventilation and respiration only if she is encouraged to take deep breaths.

Classification

Competency Category:	Curative/Supportive Care
Taxonomic Level:	Application
Client Type:	Individuals
Age Group:	Adult

References

Smeltzer, S. C., & Bare, B. G. (1996), p. 397.

Phipps, W. J., Cassmeyer, V. L., Sands, J. K., & Lehman, M. K. (1995), pp. 600-601.

7

74. correct answer: 3

1. Cleaning the incision every day is not sufficient to reduce the growth of micro-organisms; covering the incision with a dressing helps to absorb discharge and protects the surrounding tissues.

2. Cleaning the incision when necessary helps to reduce the growth of micro-organisms; but leaving an incision with discharge exposed to the air increases the chances of the growth of micro-organisms.

3. **Frequent cleaning of the incision reduces the growth of micro-organisms; changing the dressing helps to absorb the discharge and protects the wound against the entry of micro-organisms.**

4. Cleaning the incision at the client's request might not be frequent enough; this would promote the growth of micro-organisms at the incision site. Discharge that is not absorbed increases the chances of the growth of micro-organisms.

Classification

Competency Category:	Curative/Supportive Care
Taxonomic Level:	Knowledge/Comprehension
Client Type:	Individuals
Age Group:	Older Adult

References

Taylor, C., Lillis, C., & LeMone, P. (1997), pp. 709, 716.
DuGas, B. W., & Knor, E. R. (1995), pp. 1070-1072.

75. correct answer: 3

1. The amount is incorrect:see the formula given in option 3.

2. There is an error in calculating the dosage; review the formula for the calculation explained in option 3.

3. **The amount of 1.5 ml is correct. The dosage is calculated as follows: the dose ordered multiplied by the quantity available, divided by the dose available, equals the quantity to be administered (i.e., 75 mg x 2 ml ÷ 100 mg = 1.5 ml).**

4. There is an error in calculating the dosage; see the explanation given in option 3.

Classification

Competency Category:	Curative/Supportive Care
Taxonomic Level:	Application
Client Type:	Individuals
Age Group:	Adult

References

Taylor, C., Lillis, C., & LeMone, P. (1997), p. 607.
Craven, R. F., & Hirnle, C. J. (1996), p. 599.

76. correct answer: 3

1. The physician's order is the most reliable source and the only official document on the medication the client must receive. Asking the client his name is not safe, because he may be confused, or very simply mislead the nurse.

2. Calculating the dosage is very important to avoid error and maintain safety when administering the medication. Identifying the client using the name above the bed is not safe, since a mistake is possible; it is not a reliable source.

3. **Checking the medication three times helps to prevent error. The identity bracelet is the most reliable identification method. The nurse is responsible for verifying the bracelet before administering medication to the client.**

4. The frequency of administration is one of the important pieces of information to check against the physician's order, to administer the medication safely. Checking the room number is not safe.

Classification

Competency Category:	Curative/Supportive Care
Taxonomic Level:	Application
Client Type:	Individuals
Age Group:	Child & Adolescent

References

Taylor, C., Lillis, C., & LeMone, P. (1997), p. 612.
Craven, R. F., & Hirnle, C. J. (1996), pp. 601-602.

77. correct answer: 1

1. **The nurse maintains confidentiality of information by refusing to give the information to the manager. Since she does not have the client's consent, she should not involve the manager.**

2. The nurse makes this suggestion, not the client. She is limiting the client's ability to choose what he wants to do.

3. The nurse breaches confidentiality by giving information, since the manager will ultimately learn what the client is experiencing from the content of the information provided (e.g., brochures).

4. The nurse is being judgmental or interpreting the client's behaviour. She is not respecting the client's privacy.

Classification

Competency Category:	Nurse-Client Relationship
Taxonomic Level:	Knowledge/Comprehension
Client Type:	Groups, Populations, Communities
Age Group:	Adult

References

Canadian Nurses Association. (1997), *Code of Ethics for Registered Nurses*, p. 19
Craven, R. F., & Hirnle, C. (1996), p. 47.

7

78. correct answer: 3

1. The client's legs, not her pelvis, must be elevated to increase pulmonary blood volume.

2. Oxygen is administered by mask at a rate of 6 to 10 L a minute.

3. **Increasing the IV rate will increase the blood volume and help increase the blood pressure.**

4. It is preferable to position the client in labour in the left lateral position to promote utero-placental circulation since fetal hypoxia occurs during an episode of hypotension.

Classification

Competency Category:	Curative/Supportive Care
Taxonomic Level:	Application
Client Type:	Individuals
Age Group:	Adult

References

Lowdermilk, D. L., Perry, S. E., & Bobak, I. M. (1999), p. 318.

Nichols, F. H., & Zwelling, E. (1997), p. 850.

79. correct answer: 3

1. This measure is important at the beginning of the illness. However, it is important to help the client recognize the loss of field of vision and to help her become accustomed to finding objects placed on her left.

2. It is important for the client to have non-skid shoes to avoid accidents, but this decision is not directly related to perceptual dysfunctions on her left side.

3. **This exercise helps the client become aware of her surroundings and anticipate accidents.**

4. It is important for the client to have glasses that are well adjusted to her sight, but this is not linked to the problem of perceptual dysfunctions on her left side.

Classification

Competency Category:	Rehabilitative Care
Taxonomic Level:	Application
Client Type:	Individuals
Age Group:	Older Adult

References

Smeltzer, S. C., & Bare, B. G. (1996), p. 1727.

Ignatavicius, D. D., Workman, M. L., & Mishler, M. A. (1995), p. 1256.

80. correct answer: 1

1. Initially, it is important that the nurse acknowledges the client's interest in certain activities that could promote social contacts and lead to his cooperation in this respect.

2. The nurse is not promoting social interaction; she remains at a cognitive level only, which does not ensure that the client will be interested in interacting socially.

3. The nurse is imposing personal growth and self-development courses. Consequently, she is likely to limit the client's ability to decide to increase his social contacts.

4. The nurse involves the family to support the client, but she might reduce the client's ability to take responsibility for himself. The client risks being unable to develop his social skills.

Classification

Competency Category:	Rehabilitative Care
Taxonomic Level:	Application
Client Type:	Individuals
Age Group:	Adult of Advanced Age

References

Taylor, C., Lillis, C., & LeMone, P. (1997), pp. 740-744.
DuGas, B. W., & Knor, E. R. (1995), pp. 1221-1224.

81. correct answer: 3

1. The client presents an appropriate reaction to the multiple losses he has just experienced (e.g., reduced body image and self-concept).

2. There is no evidence that the client is having problems with the occupational therapist.

3. Verbalizing his feelings could help the client integrate his losses; this would facilitate his rehabilitation.

4. The nurse must first help verbalize his feelings before he embarks on an exercise program.

Classification

Competency Category:	Rehabilitative Care
Taxonomic Level:	Knowledge/Comprehension
Client Type:	Individuals
Age Group:	Adult

References

Smeltzer, S. C., & Bare, B. G. (1996), p. 1729.
DuGas, B. W., & Knor, E. R. (1995), pp. 1221-1224.

82. correct answer: 4

1. The nurse makes this suggestion to support the families, but she does not indicate what she will actually do during visits to maintain the health of the families.

2. Before establishing this service, it is essential that the nurse identify the needs of the families. They may need more than someone who just listens.

3. This idea could have merit and could meet the families' long-term needs.

4. **The nurse makes the offer of meeting with the families to listen to them and identify their needs more clearly.**

Classification

Competency Category: Professional Practice
Taxonomic Level: Application
Client Type: Families
Age Group: Not Applicable

References

Canadian Nurses Association. (1997), *Everyday Ethics: Putting the Code into Practice*, p. 13.

Canadian Nurses Association. (1997), *Code of Ethics for Registered Nurses*, p. 9.

Boyd, M. A., & Nihart, M. A. (1998), pp. 307-309.

83. correct answer: 2

1. Providing the client with Canada's Food Guide does not mean that she will understand it and will be able to choose suitable, nutritious foods.

2. **The nurse promotes independence by involving the client, while trying to obtain information about her diet.**

3. Taking a vitamin supplement cannot replace the client's ability to choose suitable, nutritious foods.

4. Attending a workshop does not mean that the client will become aware of her diet and take the steps to change her eating habits.

Classification

Competency Category: Health Promotion
Taxonomic Level: Application
Client Type: Individuals
Age Group: Child & Adolescent

References

Canadian Nurses Association. (1997), *Code of Ethics for Registered Nurses*, p. 15.

Lowdermilk, D. L., Perry, S. E., & Bobak, I. M. (1999), p. 283.

Reeder, S. J., Martin, L. L., & Koniak-Griffin, D. (1997), pp. 470-471.

84. correct answer: 4

1. This reaction is similar to denial in that it does not show personal awareness. A nurse who denies her feelings will be less aware of the actions she takes.

2. This reaction may be premature. The nurse should attempt to deal with her feelings. The nurse should talk to a colleague who can help her to become aware of what she is feeling and make the appropriate choices.

3. The client is not responsible for the nurse's feelings and must not be burdened with this problem.

4. **Talking to a colleague can help the nurse to become aware of what she is feeling and to make the appropriate choices.**

Classification

Competency Category:	Professional Practice
Taxonomic Level:	Affective
Client Type:	Individuals
Age Group:	Older Adult

References

Canadian Nurses Association. (1997), *Code of Ethics for Registered Nurses*, p. 20.

Taylor, C., Lillis, C., & LeMone, P. (1997), p. 241.

Haber, J., Krainovich-Miller, B., McMahon, A. L., & Price-Hoskins, P. (1997), pp. 129-130.

85. correct answer: 4

1. The nurse's response is not supportive and does not address the client's concerns.

2. This is false reassurance and does not address the client's concerns.

3. Reminding the client of her right to withdraw from the study could be supportive, but telling her not to worry about the doctor's possible anger may not be reassuring.

4. **Nurses provide support to clients, which enables them to act on their own behalf to meet their health care needs.**

Classification

Competency Category:	Nurse-Client Relationship
Taxonomic Level:	Critical Thinking
Client Type:	Individuals
Age Group:	Adult

References

Canadian Nurses Association. (1997), *Code of Ethics for Registered Nurses*, p. 10.

Van Servellen, G. M. (1997), pp. 326-330.

86. correct answer: 3

1. Decisions should be made jointly with suggestions from both the resident and the nurse.

2. A joint decision would be more appropriate.

3. **Assessing the client's feelings will be useful in determing whether her isolation can be detrimental and in identifying possible interventions.**

4. Needs further assessment prior to such an intervention.

Classification

Competency Category:	Nurse-Client Relationship
Taxonomic Level:	Critical Thinking
Client Type:	Individuals
Age Group:	Older Adult

References

Hogstel, M. O. (1995), pp. 22-23.

Ebersole, P., & Hess, P. (1998), pp. 650-651.

87. correct answer: 4

1. This is a trend in injury prevention.

2. There are still many people that do not consume a healthy diet for a variety of reasons. Obesity is still a large population problem.

3. Cancer is a large population problem. A balanced diet alone, however, will not address the issue.

4. **Programs that incorporate an increased sense of well-being stimulate a continued desire for improved health and are a first step to community involvement.**

Classification

Competency Category:	Health Promotion
Taxonomic Level:	Critical Thinking
Client Type:	Groups, Populations, Communities
Age Group:	Not Applicable

References

Hitchcock, J. E., & Thomas, S. A. (1999), pp. 191-192.

Stewart, M. J. (1995), pp. 496-499.

88. correct answer: 1

1. Being homeless, it is possible that the client has difficulty buying supplies and keeping them in a safe place. Providing him with information on the resources available to individuals with special circumstances will facilitate obtaining the supplies he needs.

2. The client may have little control over what food he is able to obtain. Reviewing all diet information would probably be overwhelming and is only one aspect of the overall plan.

3. His technique will be important, but at this stage, it is more important to see that he can even access the needed supplies.

4. Reviewing complications would not be done initially. He needs to be aware of complications, but this can be done at a later date.

Classification

Competency Category:	Health Promotion
Taxonomic Level:	Application
Client Type:	Individuals
Age Group:	Adult

References

Lubkin, I. M., & Larsen, P. D. (1998), pp. 345-350.

Boyd, M. A., & Nihart, M. A. (1998), pp. 109-121.

89. correct answer: 1

1. The nurse should first identify the causes of absenteeism prior to planning the program.

2. Willingness to participate in a program will be important, but the program must be developed on greatest need first.

3. It would be important to identify if this is a risk for this group of workers before a program is developed.

4. The monitoring of safety devices being used is important; however, the nurse is focusing on worker absenteism at this time.

Classification

Competency Category:	Health Promotion
Taxonomic Level:	Application
Client Type:	Groups, Populations, Communities
Age Group:	Adult

References

Spradley, B. W., & Allender, J. A. (1996), pp. 450, 452

Stanhope, M., & Lancaster, J. (1996), pp. 916-917.

7

90. correct answer: 4

1. This requires that the children understand causality, which is limited in a 3-year-old. Explaining the reason for hand washing is not sufficient to teach a 3-year-old hygienic behaviours.

2. The children might learn to associate hand-washing with using the toilet, but will not necessarily learn self-care.

3. A picture can be useful to complement learning, but active involvement in learning is known to be more effective.

4. **The children are involved actively in learning. This also enables the nurse to evaluate and reinforce the children's learning.**

Classification

Competency Category:	Health Promotion
Taxonomic Level:	Knowledge/Comprehension
Client Type:	Groups, Populations, Communities
Age Group:	Child & Adolescent

References

Pillitteri, A. (1999), p. 960.

Wong, D. L. (1995), p. 649.

91. correct answer: 4

1. Restraints are frightening to a client and can lead to increased aggression.

2. A person with cognitive impairment may interpret an attempt to reason with him as arguing, which can increase the aggression.

3. Non-pharmacologic interventions are preferable due to increased risk of adverse reactions to medications in the elderly.

4. **By leaving, the environmental stimulation is reduced which, in turn, can help the resident settle.**

Classification

Competency Category:	Illness/Injury Prevention
Taxonomic Level:	Application
Client Type:	Individuals
Age Group:	Adult of Advanced Age

References

Miller, C. A. (1999), pp. 500, 560.

Barry, P. D. (1998), p. 254.

92. correct answer: 4

1. This would be more difficult to assess accurately with crying.

2. Heart rate is not an accurate indicator of respiratory status.

3. Chest sounds will be difficult to hear while the child is crying.

4. **Skin colour will provide a quick indication of the oxygenation of the child. It gives the child some time without physical contact to settle before carrying on other assessments.**

Classification

Competency Category:	Curative/Supportive Care
Taxonomic Level:	Critical Thinking
Client Type:	Individuals
Age Group:	Child & Adolescent

References

Wong, D. L. (1995), pp. 233, 1341.

Pillitteri, A. (1999), pp. 1111-1113.

93. correct answer: 2

1. Vital signs can be done at any time. IV medications are to be given on schedule.

2. **Both of these require undressing and possibly moving the client, so would be best done while the nurse is doing the bath.**

3. The IV site change will take longer and would probably further tire the client.

4. The IV site change will take longer and would probably further tire the client.

Classification

Competency Category:	Curative/Supportive Care
Taxonomic Level:	Critical Thinking
Client Type:	Individuals
Age Group:	Older Adult

References

Smeltzer, S. C., & Bare, B. G. (1996), p. 31.

Taylor, C., Lillis, C., & LeMone, P. (1997), pp. 284-285.

94. correct answer: 4

1. For pain relief, the average adult dose of morphine sulfate is given q 3-4h.

2. The onset of pain relief when morphine sulfate is given IM is 10 to 30 minutes with the peak action occurring within 1 hour.

3. It is appropriate to do this recording but it will not solve the problem, which is the client's pain.

4. **Complementary measures help a client focus attention on something other than the pain. They have been shown to be effective in severe pain episodes when used with analgesics.**

Classification

Competency Category: Curative/Supportive Care
Taxonomic Level: Critical Thinking
Client Type: Individuals
Age Group: Adult

References

Springhouse. (1998), pp. 380-381.
Taylor, C., Lillis, C., & LeMone, P. (1997), pp. 1123-1124.

95. correct answer: 2

1. Perception of pain would be decreased by central nervous system agonists, such as morphine sulfate.

2. **Pain conduction is blocked by stimulation of large diameter fibres using massage/pressure.**

3. Pain threshold is the point at which one perceives a noxious stimuli as pain, or is the least intense stimulus that will cause pain. Massage is not known to change one's pain threshold.

4. Pain tolerance is the maximum intensity or duration of pain one is willing to endure. Tolerance for pain varies among individuals and is dependent upon a variety of physical, cultural and psycho-emotional factors. Massage is not known to reliably enhance one's tolerance to pain.

Classification

Competency Category: Curative/Supportive Care
Taxonomic Level: Knowledge/Comprehension
Client Type: Individuals
Age Group: Adult

References

Lewis, S. M., Collier, I. C., & Heitkemper, M. M. (1996), pp. 84-116.
Burrell, L. O., Gerlach, M. J., & Bless, B. S. (1997), p. 196.
Smeltzer, S. C., & Bare, B. G. (1996), pp. 179-203.

96. correct answer: 3

1. It is not necessary to avoid physical contact although it will be important to wear gloves if there is a possibility of contact with bodily fluids. Universal precautions do not apply to feces unless it contains visible blood.

2. A mask is required only when the client has or is suspected of having a communicable disease that may be transmitted through the respiratory tract.

3. **HBV is a bloodborne pathogen. It is possible to transmit the disease through direct bodily contact with bodily fluids, such as blood, breast milk, semen, or vaginal secretions. Precautions apply to other bodily fluids also, although the risk is unknown.**

4. A mask is not necessary since HBV is not air-borne. A gown is not required. Eye protection in addition to wearing gloves is recommended.

Classification

Competency Category:	Curative/Supportive Care
Taxonomic Level:	Knowledge/Comprehension
Client Type:	Individuals
Age Group:	Older Adult

References

Rosdahl, C. B. (1995), pp. 329-336.

Harkness, G. A., & Dincher, J. R. (1996), pp. 299-324.

97. correct answer: 2

1. There is a chance of alteration in sexual function with any surgical manipulation of the male urinary tract.

2. **Providing information directly with a matter-of-fact approach builds trust, reduces anxiety, and may encourage additional questions by the client.**

3. This statement blames the client and shifts responsibility to the doctor and the client.

4. It is inappropriate to make assumptions about a client's motive for asking questions.

Classification

Competency Category:	Curative/Supportive Care
Taxonomic Level:	Knowledge/Comprehension
Client Type:	Individuals
Age Group:	Adult

References

Lewis, S. M., Collier, I. C., & Heitkemper, M. M. (1996), pp. 1626-1637.

Smeltzer, S. C., & Bare, B. G. (1996), pp. 1344-1347.

7

98. correct answer: 2

1. This can be a very supportive measure, but in itself is not usually effective.

2. **Preventing symptoms from starting is most effective as the nausea and vomiting in palliative clients is self-perpetuating. The most effective relief is provided with medications that work on the probable etiology.**

3. This is an appropriate nursing strategy to supplement proper medication administration, but not always effective on its own.

4. Activity may or may not be part of the client's etiology.

Classification

Competency Category:	Curative/Supportive Care
Taxonomic Level:	Application
Client Type:	Families
Age Group:	Not Applicable

References

Kemp, C. (1995), pp. 177-179.

Ferris, F. D., & Cummings, I. (1995), p. 54.

99. correct answer: 4

1. Initial shock has to dissipate prior to dealing with any part of the grieving process. It is unrealistic to expect that the parents will come to terms with their child's death at this time.

2. Although it may be helpful to have the assistance of the supervisor, this shifts responsibility away from the nurse.

3. Although pastoral care could be helpful in the situation, this assumes that the parents would want such intervention.

4. **The appropriate nursing intervention in the "Shock & Disbelief" stage of grieving any loss is to provide emotional support and an opportunity for the grieving person(s) to vent their feelings.**

Classification

Competency Category:	Curative/Supportive Care
Taxonomic Level:	Application
Client Type:	Families
Age Group:	Child & Adolescent

References

Rosdahl, C. B. (1995), p. 827.

Wong, D. L. (1995), p. 995.

100. correct answer: 2

1. Lifeguarding is not within the nurse's scope of practice. There is an inherent obligation to protect and be accountable to the public.

2. **The nurse should clarify to those to whom she is accountable the limits of her scope of competence. As well, the law obligates the nurse to practise within the scope of nursing; lifeguarding duties are not part of the nurse's scope of practice.**

3. Although this may be a reasonable solution to the problem, the nurse should first ensure the leadership team understands the nurse's role.

4. The nurse should first ensure the leadership team understands the nurse's role. In addition, it would have to be determined that all members of the leadership team were qualified to lifeguard before making this suggestion.

Classification

Competency Category: Professional Practice
Taxonomic Level: Application
Client Type: Groups, Populations, Communities
Age Group: Child & Adolescent

References

Arnold, E., & Boggs, K. U. (1995), p. 138.

Canadian Nurses Association. (1997), *Code of Ethics for Registered Nurses*, p. 23.

Canadian Nurses Association. (1993), *The Scope of Nursing Practice: A Review of Issues and Trends*, p. 10.

101. correct answer: 2

1. This may result in premature closure without resolution.

2. **A principle in the mediation process. One communication technique is to be honest and confront colleagues when friction first occurs rather than let it escalate.**

3. This may cause the conflict to escalate further.

4. The team has already been venting, and this may perpetuate the conflict.

Classification

Competency Category: Professional Practice
Taxonomic Level: Affective
Client Type: Groups, Populations, Communities
Age Group: Child & Adolescent

References

Van Servellen, G. M. (1997), p. 295.
Riley, J. W., Balzer. (1996), p. 208.

102. correct answer: 3

1. Although these measures may be soothing, the nurse needs to rule out the possibility of the rash being due to an infectious disease. Varicella should be suspected due to the symptoms and incidence in immunosuppressed children.

2. A rash on the trunk is not characteristic of mosquito bites. Further assessment to determine the cause of the rash is needed.

3. **The child is demonstrating signs of varicella; it needs to be determined whether he would have either natural or vaccine-induced immunity to varicella. The oncologist should be contacted if varicella is suspected, because of the risk it poses to immunocompromised clients. If varicella is suspected, the child is contagious and needs to be isolated.**

4. The use of Aspirin is contraindicated in children, especially during a viral illness, due to the risk of Reye's syndrome.

Classification

Competency Category:	Professional Practice
Taxonomic Level:	Critical Thinking
Client Type:	Groups, Populations, Communities
Age Group:	Child & Adolescent

References

Wong, D. L. (1999), pp. 722-723, 1726.
Marks, M. G. (1998), p. 307.

103. correct answer: 2

1. Universal precautions are not required with vomitus, urine, or sputum, as these fluids are not normally associated with transmission of bloodborne pathogens.

2. **The use of gloves is an important strategy to prevent transmission of bloodborne pathogens.**

3. Although gloves should be worn when assisting any client with personal hygiene, latex gloves are not necessary. Gloves are not necessary unless there is visible blood in the body fluids.

4. Barrier precautions protect immunocompromised clients from micro-organisms, but do not protect the nurse.

Classification

Competency Category:	Illness/Injury Prevention
Taxonomic Level:	Application
Client Type:	Groups, Populations, Communities
Age Group:	Child & Adolescent

References

Smeltzer, S. C., & Bare, B. G. (1996), p. 1961.
Kozier, B., & Erb, G. (1998), pp. 680-683.

104. correct answer: 4

1. This response does not deal with the client's request. Sexual intercourse in not contraindicated for clients who are receiving chemotherapy.

2. Parental consent is not required. In Canada, the law states that the age of consent for sexual activity is 14 years old.

3. Clients' confidentiality would be breached if the nurse discussed this issue without consent of the client.

4. **The nurse should use this opportunity to discuss issues of sexual health with the client. The nurse has a responsibility to promote safe sex practices among sexually active clients.**

Classification

Competency Category: Health Promotion
Taxonomic Level: Knowledge/Comprehension
Client Type: Groups, Populations, Communities
Age Group: Child & Adolescent

References

Boyd, M. A., & Nihart, M. A. (1998), p. 804.
Grant, A. E., & Ashman, A. A. (1997), p. 151.

105. correct answer: 2

1. Cathy's activity plan should not be altered unnecessarily. If Cathy can safely manage her dressing change, the nurse should encourage her to participate in the planned activity.

2. **A 12-year-old has the cognitive ability and dexterity to manage a central line dressing change. Involving children of this age in their care encourages independence and fosters self-reliance.**

3. While the counsellor could learn this task, such a solution does not foster independence.

4. There is no need to modify the regimen of dressing changes. Moreover, the dressing could become loose or dirtied during the canoe trip, necessitating that someone on the trip have the skill to change it.

Classification

Competency Category: Rehabilitative Care
Taxonomic Level: Application
Client Type: Groups, Populations, Communities
Age Group: Child & Adolescent

References

Wong, D. L. (1999), pp. 1308-1311.
Chestnut, M. A. (1998), p. 127.

7

106. correct answer: 4

1. Lonnie is still displaying active symptoms of asthma. If his treatment was adequate, the nurse would not expect him to be experiencing these symptoms.

2. The environmental control will be important, but this is a blaming-type statement.

3. The nurse has no evidence to support the fact that Lonnie's medications are not appropriate.

4. **The nurse is asking the mother to reveal more about her beliefs and understanding about the symptoms of asthma, and her assessment of the child's health. This will assist the nurse in the evaluation of the treatment.**

Classification

Competency Category:	Curative/Supportive Care
Taxonomic Level:	Critical Thinking
Client Type:	Families
Age Group:	Child & Adolescent

References

Wong, D. L. (1999), pp. 1503-1512.

Taylor, C., Lillis, C., & LeMone, P. (1997), pp. 370-371.

107. correct answer: 3

1. The quality of air in Lonnie's room has not been determined to be the reason for his night coughing.

2. Cat hair/saliva remain in the environment even after a cat is no longer present. Removing the cat just before bedtime would not be sufficient.

3. **The use of peak flow monitoring before and after bronchodilator use provides an objective measure of airway constriction. It is simple to do and would allow Lonnie and his mother to gain greater understanding of his condition.**

4. Before making this recommendation, the nurse should explore with Lonnie's mother why she is smoking. This is a blaming approach that may create guilt.

Classification

Competency Category:	Rehabilitative Care
Taxonomic Level:	Application
Client Type:	Families
Age Group:	Child & Adolescent

References

Wong, D. L. (1999), pp. 1503-1512.

Pillitteri, A. (1995), pp. 1289-1292.

108. correct answer: 2

1. The dust from the sandbox may be a trigger for the client. Dusty environments should be avoided.

2. **Baseball has start and stop activity requiring short bursts of energy and limited running.**

3. The continuous running of soccer would require more endurance than the client is demonstrating, and would reinforce his feeling of not being able to keep up with the other children.

4. Computer games provide limited social activity and no significant physical activity. Children with asthma should be encouraged to exercise in order to promote physical fitness and activity tolerance.

Classification

Competency Category:	Health Promotion
Taxonomic Level:	Application
Client Type:	Families
Age Group:	Child & Adolescent

References

Wong, D. L. (1999), pp. 1503-1512.

Lubkin, I. M., & Larsen, P. D. (1998), pp. 46-47.

109. correct answer: 4

1. This is anecdotal information and is not research-based.

2. This is the nurse's observation. It is anecdotal and is not research-based.

3. This is not evidence-based nursing knowledge. It is recommending the use of an expert.

4. **Research has shown that the use of beta-agonists, such as Ventolin, will prevent the exercise-induced bronchospasm in more than 80% of clients.**

Classification

Competency Category:	Professional Practice
Taxonomic Level:	Critical Thinking
Client Type:	Families
Age Group:	Child & Adolescent

References

Wong, D. L. (1999), p. 1509.

Lubkin, I. M., & Larsen, P. D. (1998), pp. 46-47.

7

110. correct answer: 2

1. It may give the children the information, but does not contribute to Lonnie's peer relationship development.

2. **By allowing Lonnie the opportunity to teach the other children, he learns more himself and will deliver the knowledge at an appropriate level. He will also learn to communicate effectively with his peers about asthma.**

3. It would be impossible to verify that the children actually receive the correct information or ask any questions that they may have. It does nothing to facilitate Lonnie's peer relationships.

4. By developing and implementing a plan, the nurse is not allowing Lonnie any joint control of the situation.

Classification

Competency Category: Health Promotion

Taxonomic Level: Application

Client Type: Groups, Populations, Communities

Age Group: Child & Adolescent

References

Wong, D. L. (1999), pp. 1503-1511.

Lubkin, I. M., & Larsen, P. D. (1998), pp. 46-47

111. correct answer: 1

1. **Children at 6 years of age enjoy activities with adults. Children enjoy assisting with meal preparation, and associate this activity with being grown-up.**

2. Television programming after 9 p.m. is geared toward an adult audience and would not be appropriate for a child of 6 years.

3. Children of 6 are beginning to read. However, the focus is again on Lonnie's asthma, which he has complained is the reason his parents treat him like a baby.

4. Building model airplanes is an appropriate activity for children 8 years and older. The glue used in building model airplanes may trigger the client's asthma.

Classification

Competency Category: Rehabilitative Care

Taxonomic Level: Critical Thinking

Client Type: Families

Age Group: Child & Adolescent

References

Wong, D. L. (1999), p. 793.

Bowden, V. R., Dickey, S. B., & Smith Greenberg, C. (1998), pp. 301, 308-309.

112. correct answer: 4

1. The nurse is making a general assumption about all nurses.

2. Demonstrates resignation and will not prompt the nurse to take action.

3. The nurse is avoiding the issue.

4. **Self-disclosure means to open up to self and others and make feelings known. This may allow the nurse to overcome her feelings of discomfort.**

Classification

Competency Category: Professional Practice
Taxonomic Level: Affective
Client Type: Groups, Populations, Communities
Age Group: Older Adult

References

Arnold, E., & Boggs, K. U. (1995), p. 83.
Riley, J. W., Balzer. (1996), pp. 139-141.

113. correct answer: 2

1. Clinical manifestations occur late in the progression of prostate cancer. Early detection is possible through routine screening.

2. **Annual screening for prostate cancer by digital rectal exam (DRE) and detection for elevated serum levels of prostate-specific antigen (PSA) is recommended by the Canadian Task Force on Periodic Exams.**

3. Treatment information is appropriate for individuals who have received a diagnosis of prostate cancer.

4. This information may cause unnecessary fear in the group. There is evidence to show that many elderly men have some cancer cells in their prostate, yet the cancer does not lead to clinical disease.

Classification

Competency Category: Health Promotion
Taxonomic Level: Critical Thinking
Client Type: Groups, Populations, Communities
Age Group: Older Adult

References

Nettina, S. M. (1996), pp. 99-100.
Miller, C. A. (1999), p. 667.

7

114. correct answer: 1

1. Acknowledging the group's feelings demonstrates respect for human dignity.
2. Avoids the issue.
3. Avoids the issue.
4. Avoids the issue.

Classification

Competency Category: Professional Practice
Taxonomic Level: Affective
Client Type: Groups, Populations, Communities
Age Group: Older Adult

References

Arnold, E., & Boggs, K. U. (1995), p. 80.
Canadian Nurses Association. (1997), *Code of Ethics for Registered Nurses*, p. 6.

115. correct answer: 3

1. Impotence only occurs with radical prostatectomy when surgical damage to the nerves surrounding the prostate has been unavoidable.
2. There is a physiologic basis for impotence. However, it is no longer a common occurrence with all treatments for prostate cancer.
3. It is necessary to provide accurate answers to the client's questions. This statement also reflects the nurse's acceptance of the client's right to information.
4. This statement does not answer the question.

Classification

Competency Category: Curative/Supportive Care
Taxonomic Level: Application
Client Type: Groups, Populations, Communities
Age Group: Older Adult

References

Arnold, E., & Boggs, K. U. (1995), p. 227.
Riley, J. W., Balzer. (1996), p. 42.
Burrell, L. O., Gerlach, M. J., & Pless, B. S. (1997), p. 1785.

116. correct answer: 2

1. This statement demonstrates the nurse taking over this responsibility and would not promote continuity of care.
2. This action promotes continuity by referring the men to their own physicians.
3. Although this is a possibility, this is highly unlikely to occur and does not promote continuity of care.
4. This statement demonstrates the program director taking over this responsibility.

Classification

Competency Category: Curative/Supportive Care
Taxonomic Level: Application
Client Type: Groups, Populations, Communities
Age Group: Older Adult

References

Cookfair, J. M. (1996), pp. 551-560.
Stackhouse, J. C. (1998), pp. 284-288.

117. correct answer: 2

1. Activity levels have not been associated with a reduced risk of prostate cancer.

2. Annual screening for prostate cancer by digital rectal exams (DRE) and for elevated serum levels of prostate-specific antigen (PSA) are recommended by the Canadian Task Force on Periodic Exams for men over 60 years.

3. This is a sign of prostate cancer, but is more likely a symptom of benign prostatic hypertrophy, the most common disorder in aging male clients.

4. Studies looking at pesticides have been inconclusive in demonstrating an increased risk for prostate cancer.

Classification

Competency Category:	Rehabilitative Care
Taxonomic Level:	Critical Thinking
Client Type:	Groups, Populations, Communities
Age Group:	Older Adult

References

Burrell, L. O., Gerlach, M. J., & Pless, B. S. (1997), p. 1781.

Canadian Nurses Association. (1997), *Everyday Ethics: Putting the Code into Practice*, p. 15.

Rosdahl, C. B. (1995), pp. 36-37.

118. correct answer: 1

1. **Multidisciplinary team conferences enable sharing of information and joint decision making; comprehensive care plans can be developed and reviewed.**

2. Identification of discipline-specific health needs are the responsibility of the particular discipline.

3. Client care can easily become fragmented when health team members communicate between themselves on an individual basis only, and not within the team.

4. The nurse is not responsible for making decisions for all health team members. This does not allow for joint decision-making.

Classification

Competency Category:	Rehabilitative Care
Taxonomic Level:	Application
Client Type:	Individuals
Age Group:	Not Applicable

References

DuGas, B. W., & Knor, E. R. (1995), p. 417.

Taylor, C., Lillis, C., & LeMone, P. (1997), pp. 302-303.

7

119. correct answer: 1

1. Parents should be able to choose whether or not to stay during invasive procedures. This option lets the parent know it is all right to leave and that someone will stay with the child.

2. This could be perceived as pressure to stay even though the nurse is acknowledging the parent's distress.

3. This approach acknowledges the parent's emotional state but does not offer an option.

4. Although the presence of parents is usually supportive to the child, parents can become distressed by being there. Their distress can cause the child to become more upset.

Classification

Competency Category:	Rehabilitative Care
Taxonomic Level:	Application
Client Type:	Families
Age Group:	Child & Adolescent

References

Wong, D. L. (1995), pp. 1138-1139.

Pillitteri, A. (1999), pp. 987-988.

120. correct answer: 4

1. The cane should be held with the hand on the unaffected side to provide maximum support and balance.

2. The cane should be advanced forward first before the affected leg to prevent the risk of falling.

3. The affected leg should be moved forward only after advancing the cane to support the body weight on the cane and the unaffected leg.

4. Advancing the cane first provides the client with maximum support.

Classification

Competency Category:	Rehabilitative Care
Taxonomic Level:	Knowledge/Comprehension
Client Type:	Individuals
Age Group:	Older Adult

References

Taylor, C., Lillis, C., & LeMone, P. (1997), p. 1055.

Potter, P. A., & Perry, A. G. (1999), p. 705.

121. correct answer: 4

1. The nurse is acknowledging that the physio-therapy does hurt but is not offering support to the mother.

2. This gives the mother the option not to attend the physiotherapy, but it withdraws family support from the child.

3. Even if it is reduced, Joseph must still continue to have physiotherapy, so his mother's dilemma is not resolved.

4. **This explores the possibility of an alternative option that will allow the mother not to be present while the child still has family support.**

Classification

Competency Category:	Rehabilitative Care
Taxonomic Level:	Application
Client Type:	Families
Age Group:	Child & Adolescent

References

Wong, D. L. (1995), p. 1275.

Van Servellen, G. M. (1997), p. 306.

122. correct answer: 1

1. **The nurse should perform a physical assessment. A vomiting client is at risk for aspiration. His level of consciousness (Glasgow coma scale) should also be assessed continually due to the risk of alcohol toxicity.**

2. The nurse must be able to continually monitor the client for neurological status. Also, a vomiting client is at risk for aspiration.

3. Vital signs should be monitored, but oral fluids are contraindicated with a vomiting client. Referral to a community addiction centre is not appropriate until the client has been assessed and stabilized.

4. The client needs to be assessed prior to adminis-tering a medication, which may sedate him.

Classification

Competency Category:	Professional Practice
Taxonomic Level:	Application
Client Type:	Families
Age Group:	Adult

References

Canadian Nurses Association. (1997), *Code of Ethics for Registered Nurses*, p. 17.

Lewis, S. M., Collier, I. C., & Heitkemper, M. M. (1996), p. 626.

7

123. correct answer: 1

1. An overdose of insulin will cause hypoglycemia. Administration of oral glucose is accepted treatment for hypoglycemia and is within the scope of nursing practice. These actions are consistent with professional responsibilities and standards of practice, and satisfy the code of ethics value of accountability.

2. The physician and agency need to be informed.

3. An overdose of insulin will cause hypoglycemia and corrective actions need to be quickly initiated prior to taking a stat capillary glucose. It is the physician's responsibility to plan insulin rescheduling. A medication incident report is also required.

4. The physician and agency need to be informed.

Classification

Competency Category:	Professional Practice
Taxonomic Level:	Application
Client Type:	Families
Age Group:	Adult

References

Canadian Nurses Association. (1997), *Code of Ethics for Registered Nurses*, p. 7.

Tierney, L. M., McPhee, S. J., & Papadakis, M. A. (1998), p. 1119.

124. correct answer: 3

1. This statement leads the student to believe that professionalism does not encourage admitting one's limitations. This is not conducive to a safe environment.

2. Although this may be helpful, it does not assist the student to evaluate his abilities; the nurse just takes over care.

3. This allows the student to discuss his concerns about his inability to meet the requirements and allows the development of a joint plan of care.

4. This does not allow the student to voice his concerns about his capabilities. It also prevents forming a learning plan for the student nurse to meet his practice needs.

Classification

Competency Category:	Professional Practice
Taxonomic Level:	Application
Client Type:	Individuals
Age Group:	Adult

References

Canadian Nurses Association. (1997), *Code of Ethics for Registered Nurses*, p. 22.

Doheney, M. O'Bryan (1997), pp. 228-231.

125. correct answer: 4

1. This intervention makes no allowance for the feelings of Sarah and her family.

2. This intervention ignores hospital policy and assumes that Sarah and her family wish to continue to visit.

3. This intervention ignores hospital policy.

4. **It is necessary to be flexible in following policies that may have detrimental results. It is important to determine that outcomes are understood and desired by both the parents and the child.**

Classification

Competency Category: Professional Practice
Taxonomic Level: Critical Thinking
Client Type: Families
Age Group: Child & Adolescent

References

Canadian Nurses Association. (1997), *Code of Ethics for Registered Nurses*, pp. 17-21.
Wong, D. L. (1995), pp. 186-191.

126. correct answer: 4

1. A client who presents with an airway disturbance should be attended to immediately.

2. The nurse is acting against her better judgment by not ensuring that the client is examined by a physician. The client's condition could deteriorate because he did not receive appropriate treatment.

3. There may not be another physician available. Another physician may or may not choose to counter the opinion of a colleague.

4. **By consulting with the charge nurse, the nurse confirms her judgment that the client should receive immediate treatment. In taking this action, the nurse recognizes her scope of practice and professional responsibilities.**

Classification

Competency Category: Professional Practice
Taxonomic Level: Critical Thinking
Client Type: Individuals
Age Group: Adult

References

Canadian Nurses Association. (1997), *Code of Ethics for Registered Nurses*, p. 23.
Canadian Nurses Association. (1997), *Everyday Ethics: Putting the Code into Practice*, p. 51.

7

127. correct answer: 1

1. Entries in nurses' notes must be made promptly and include accurately documented observations and interventions.

2. Reporting to a colleague is appropriate, but observations and care should be documented soon after the completion, and prior to leaving the unit.

3. Documenting interventions only does not apply the principle of completeness.

4. Taking a break first does not apply the principle of timely recording of observations and care provided.

Classification

Competency Category:	Professional Practice
Taxonomic Level:	Application
Client Type:	Individuals
Age Group:	Child & Adolescent

References

DuGas, B. W., & Knor, E. R. (1995), pp. 456-457.
Craven, R. F., & Hirnle, C. (1996), pp. 220-225.

128. correct answer: 2

1. Answering the phone will delay responding to the client with chest pain, which is potentially more life-threatening than the phone call.

2. **Chest pain is the most potentially life-threatening problem presented here. Postoperative pain, while not life-threatening, may be prevented from escalating by administering medication before it peaks.**

3. The client has vomited her supper, not blood. While this is unpleasant, it does not need immediate attention.

4. Answering the phone is not the second priority after assessing the client with chest pain. Attending to the immediate needs of the clients in the unit takes precedence over answering the telephone call.

Classification

Competency Category:	Professional Practice
Taxonomic Level:	Application
Client Type:	Groups, Populations, Communities
Age Group:	Adult

References

Lewis, S. M., Collier, I. C., & Heitkemper, M. M. (1996), pp. 903-907.
Bates, G. F. (1997), p. 156.

129. correct answer: 3

1. Attending to this client is important but the nurse should recognize that the other clients also require immediate attention. The nurse should determine this situation as an unrealistic workload in this situation and call for assistance.

2. This is an unmanageable workload and the nurse requires assistance. The IV should be initially stopped and removed later.

3. **This is an unmanageable workload and the nurse requires assistance. Nurses have the responsibility to work within their limitations to ensure a safe working environment.**

4. Assisting this client to a chair without an adequate assessment of the client's injury would increase the risk of further harm. While assisting the client who has fallen is a priority, the initial action of the nurse should be to call for assistance due to the unmanageable workload.

Classification

Competency Category:	Professional Practice
Taxonomic Level:	Critical Thinking
Client Type:	Groups, Populations, Communities
Age Group:	Adult

References

DuGas, B. W., & Knor, E. R. (1995), p. 124.

Canadian Nurses Association. (1997), *Everyday Ethics: Putting the Code into Practice*, p. 25.

130. correct answer: 4

1. The physician does not have responsibility for staffing duties. This does not resolve the situation.

2. The family does not have the responsibility to provide care. It is important to assign the right task to the right person.

3. Care of unstable clients requiring advanced interventions requires an RN.

4. **By reassigning the client, the charge nurse ensures the client receives appropriate care.**

Classification

Competency Category:	Professional Practice
Taxonomic Level:	Critical Thinking
Client Type:	Individuals
Age Group:	Adult

References

Canadian Nurses Association. (1997), *Code of Ethics for Registered Nurses*, p. 19.

Ellis, J. R., & Hartley, C. L. (1998), p. 447.

7

Bibliography

Bibliography

Antai-Otong, D. (1995). *Assessment and Medications for Psychiatric Nursing.* Philadelphia, PA: Saunders.

Armentrout, G. (1998). *Community Based Nursing.* Stamford, CT: Appleton & Lange.

Arnold, E., & Boggs, K. U. (1995). *Interpersonal Relationships: Professional Communication Skills for Nurses* (2nd ed.). Toronto, ON: Saunders.

Barry, P. D. (1998). *Mental Health & Mental Illness* (6th ed.). Philadelphia, PA: Lippincott.

Bates, G. F. (1997). *Mason's Basic Medical-Surgical Nursing* (6th ed.). New York, NY: McGraw-Hill.

Bobak, I. M., Lowdermilk, D. L., Jensen, M. D., & Perry, S. E. (1995). *Maternity Nursing* (4th ed.). St. Louis, MO: Mosby.

Bowden, V. R., Dickey, S. B., & Smith Greenberg, C. (1998). *Children and Their Families: The Continuum of Care.* Toronto, ON: Saunders.

Boyd, M. A., & Nihart, M. A. (1998). *Psychiatric Nursing: Contemporary Practice.* Philadelphia, PA: Lippincott.

Boyd, M. D., Graham, B. A., Gleit, C. J., & Whitman, N. I. (1998). *Health Teaching in Nursing Practice: A Professional Model* (3rd ed.). Stamford, CT: Appleton & Lange.

Burrell, L. O., Gerlack, M. J., & Pless, B. S. (1997). *Foundations of Contemporary Nursing Practice: Adult Nursing,* Volume I, (2nd ed.). Toronto, ON: Appleton & Lange.

Burton, G. G., Hodgkin, J. E., & Ward, J. J. (1997). *Respiratory Care: A Guide to Clinical Practice* (4th ed.). Philadelphia, PA: Lippincott.

Canadian Nurses Association. (1999). *Blueprint for the Canadian Registered Nurse Examination.* Ottawa, ON: Author.

Canadian Nurses Association. (1997). *Code of Ethics for Registered Nurses.* Ottawa, ON: Author.

Canadian Nurses Association. (1997). *Everyday Ethics: Putting the Code into Practice.* Ottawa, ON: Author.

Canadian Nurses Association. (1995). *Position Paper: A Framework for Health Care Delivery.* Ottawa, ON: Author.

Canadian Pharmacists Association. (1999). *Compendium of Pharmaceuticals and Specialties* (34th ed.). Toronto, ON: Webcom Limited.

Canadian Public Health Association. (1990). *Community Health — Public Health Nursing in Canada.* Ottawa, ON: Author.

Carpentino, L. J. (1997). *Nursing Diagnosis: Application to Clinical Practice* (7th ed.). Philadelphia, PA: Lippincott.

Carpentino, L. J. (1995). *Nursing Diagnosis: Application to Clinical Practice* (6th ed.). Philadelphia, PA: Lippincott.

Chestnut, M. A. (1998). *Pediatric Home Care Manual.* Philadelphia, PA: Lippincott.

Clemen-Stone, S., Eigsti, D. G., & McGuire, S. L. (1995). *Comprehensive Community Health Nursing: Family, Aggregate, & Community Practice* (4th ed.). St. Louis, MO: Mosby.

College of Nurses of Ontario. (1996). *Professional Standards for the Registered Nurses and Registered Practical Nurses in Ontario.* Toronto, ON: Author.

College of Nurses of Ontario. (1995). *Guidelines for Professional Behaviour*. Toronto, ON: Author.

Colombaro, G.C. (1998). *Pediatrics: Core Content At-A-Glance*. Philadelphia, PA: Lippincott.

Cookfair, J. M. (1996). *Nursing Care in the Community*. St. Louis, MO: Mosby.

Craven, R. F., & Hirnle, C. (1996). *Fundamentals of Nursing: Human Health and Functions*. Philadelphia, PA: Lippincott.

Deglin, J. H., & Vallerand, A. H. (1997). *Davis's Drug Guide For Nurses* (5th ed.). Philadelphia, PA: F.A. Davis Company.

Doenges, M. E. (1997). *Nursing Care Plans: Guidelines for Individualizing Patient Care* (4th ed.). New York, NY: F. A. Davis.

Doheney, M., O'Bryan (1997). *The Discipline of Nursing: An Introduction*. New York, NY: Appleton & Lange.

Drummond, K. E. (1994). *Nutrition for the Food Service Professional* (2nd ed.). New York, NY: Reenhold.

Dudek, S.G. (1997). *Nutrition Handbook for Nursing Practice*. Philadelphia, PA: Lippincott.

DuGas, B. W., & Knor, E. R. (1995). *Nursing Foundations: A Canadian Perspective*. Scarborough, ON: Appleton & Lange Canada.

Ebersole, P., & Hess, P. (1998). *Toward Healthy Aging: Human Needs and Nursing Response*. St. Louis, MO: Mosby.

Eisenhauer, L. A., Nichols, L.W., & Bergon, F. W. (1998). *Clinical Pharmacology & Nursing Management* (5th ed.). Philadelphia, PA: Lippincott.

Eliopoulos, C. (1997). *Gerontological Nursing* (4th ed.). Philadelphia, PA: Lippincott.

Elkin, M. K., Perry, A. G., & Potter, P. A. (1996). *Nursing Interventions and Clinical Skills*. St. Louis, MO: Mosby.

Ellis, J. R., & Hartley, C. L. (1998). *Nursing in Today's World: Challenges, Issues, and Trends*. Philadelphia, PA: Lippincott.

Ferris, F. D., & Cumming, I. (1995). *Palliative Care: Towards a Consensus on Standardized Principles of Practice*. Ottawa, ON: Canadian Palliative Care Association.

Friedman, M. M. (1998). *Family Nursing: Research, Theory & Practice* (4th ed.). Stamford, CT: Appleton & Lange.

Giger, J. N., & Davidhizar, R. E. (1995). *Transcultural Nursing: Assessment and Intervention* (2nd ed.). St. Louis. MO: Mosby.

Grant, A. E., & Ashman, A. A. (1997). *A Nurse's Practical Guide to the Law*. Aurora, ON: Aurora Professional Press.

Haber, J., Krainovich-Miller, B., McMahon, A. L., & Price-Hoskins, P. (1997). *Comprehensive Psychiatric Nursing* (5th ed.). St. Louis, MO: Mosby.

Hall, J. K. (1996). *Nursing Ethics and Law*. Toronto, ON: W. B. Saunders Company.

Harkness, G. A., & Dincher, J. R. (1996). *Medical Surgical Nursing: Total Patient Care* (9th ed.). St. Louis, MO: Mosby.

Health Action Lobby. (HEAL). (1996). *Securing Medicare's Future: A Submission to the House of Commons Standing Committee on Finance and the Minister of Finance*. Ottawa, ON: Author.

Hitchcock, J. E., Schubert, P. E., & Thomas, S. A. (1999). *Community Health Nursing: Caring in Action*. New York, NY: Delmar Publishers.

Hoeman, S. P. (1996). *Rehabilitation Nursing: Process and Application* (2nd ed.). St. Louis, MO: Mosby.

Hogstel, M. O. (1995). *Geropsychiatric Nursing* (2nd ed.). St. Louis, MO: Mosby.

Hudak, C. M., Gallo, B. M., & Morton, P. G. (1998). *Critical Care Nursing: A Holistic Approach*. Philadelphia, PA: Lippincott.

Hunt, R., & Zurek E. L. (1997). *Introduction to Community Health Based Nursing*. Philadelphia, PA: Lippincott.

Ignatavicius, D. D., Workman, M. L., & Mishler, M. A. (1995). *Medical-Surgical Nursing: A Nursing Process Approach* (2nd ed.). Philadelphia, PA: W. B. Saunders.

Johnson, B. S. (1997). *Psychiatric Mental Health Nursing* (4th ed.). Philadelphia, PA: Lippincott.

Johnson, J. Y. , Smith-Temple, J., & Carr, P. (1998). *Nurse's Guide to Home Health Procedures* (2nd ed.). Philadelphia, PA: Lippincott.

Karch, A. (1999). *1999 Lippincott's Nursing Drug Guide*. Philadelphia, PA: Lippincott.

Keatings, M., & Smith, O. (2000). *Ethical and Legal Issues in Canadian Nursing* (2nd ed.). Toronto, ON: Saunders.

Kemp, C. (1995). *Terminal Illness: A Guide to Nursing Care*. Philadelphia, PA. Lippincott.

Kozier, B. & Erb, G. (1998). *Fundamentals of Nursing: Concepts, Process and Practice* (5th ed.). Redwood City, CA: Addison Wesley.

Lewis, S. M., Collier, I. C., & Heitkemper, M. M. *Medical-Surgical Nursing: Assessment and Management of Clinical Problems* (4th ed.). (1996). St. Louis, MO: Mosby.

Lowdermilk, D. L., Perry, S. E., & Bobak, I.M. (1999). *Maternity Nursing* (5th ed.). St. Louis, MO: Mosby.

Lowdermilk, D. L., Perry, S. E., Bobak, I. M. (1997). *Maternity & Women's Health Care* (6th ed.). St. Louis, MO: Mosby.

Lubkin, I. M., & Larsen, P. D. (1998). *Chronic Illness: Impact and Interventions*. Toronto, ON: Jones and Bartlett Publishers.

Lueknotte, A. G. (1996). *Gerontological Nursing*. St. Louis, MO: Mosby.

Marks, M. G. (1998). *Broadribb's Introductory Pediatric Nursing* (5th ed.). Philadelphia, PA: Lippincott.

Matteson, M. A., McConnell, E. S., & Linton, A. D. (1997). *Gerontological Nursing: Concepts and Practice* (2nd ed.). Philadelphia, PA: Saunders.

Miller, C.A. (1999). *Nursing Care of Older Adults: Theory and Practice* (3rd ed.). Philadelphia, PA: Lippincott.

Murray, R. B., & Zestner, J. P. (1997). *Health Assessment and Promotion Strategies Through the Life Span*. Stamford, CT: Appleton and Lange.

Nettina, S. M. (1997). *Lippincott's Pocket Manual of Nursing Practice*. Philadelphia, PA: Lippincott.

Nettina, S.M. (1996). *The Lippincott Manual of Nursing Practice* (6th ed.). Philadelphia, PA: Lippincott.

Nichols, F. H., and Zwelling, E. (1997). *Maternal-Newborn Nursing: Theory and Practice*. Philadelphia, PA: Saunders.

Nurses Association of New Brunswick/l'Association des infirmières et infirmiers du Nouveau-Brunswick. (1995). *Nurse-Client Relationships*. Fredericton, NB: Author.

Nursing 98 Books (1998). *Nursing 98 Drug Handbook*. Philadelphia, PA: Springhouse.

Olds, S. B., London, M. L., & Ladewig, P. W. (1996). *Maternal Newborn Nursing: A Family-Centered Approach* (5th ed.). Don Mills, ON: Addison-Wesley Nursing.

Ordre des infirmières et infirmiers du Québec. (1996). *Outlook on the Practice of Nursing*. Montreal, QC: Author.

Pender, N. J. (1996). *Health Promotion in Nursing Practice* (3rd ed.). Stamford, CT: Appleton & Lange.

Philips, D. L. (1997). *Manual of I.V. Therapeutics* (2nd ed.). Philadelphia, PA: F. A. Davis.

Phipps, W. J., Cassmeyer, V. L., Sands, J. K., & Lehman, M. K. (1995). *Medical-Surgical Nursing: Concepts and Clinical Practice* (5th ed.). St. Louis, MO: Mosby.

Pillitteri, A. (1999). *Maternal and Child Health Nursing: Care of the Childbearing and Childbearing Family* (3rd ed.). Philadelphia, PA: Lippincott.

Pilliteri, A. (1995). *Maternal and Child Health Nursing: Care of the Childbearing and Childbearing Family* (2nd ed.). Philadelphia, PA: Lippincott.

Potter, P. A., & Perry, A. G. (1999). *Basic Nursing: A Critical Thinking Approach*. St. Louis, MO: Mosby.

Potter, P. A., & Perry, A. G. (1995). *Basic Nursing: Theory and Practice* (3rd ed.). St. Louis, MO: Mosby.

Registered Nurses Association of British Columbia. (1998). *Competencies Required of a New Graduate*. Vancouver, BC: Author.

Reeder, S. J., Martin, L. L., & Koniak-Griffin, D. (1997). *Maternity Nursing: Family, Newborn & Women's Health Care* (18th ed.). Philadelphia, PA: Lippincott.

Riley, J.W., Balzer (1996). *Communications in Nursing*. St. Louis, MO: Mosby.

Riordan, J., & Averbach, K. G. (1999). *Breastfeading and Human Lactation* (2nd ed.). Sudbury, MA: Jones and Bartlett Publishers.

Rosdahl, C. B. (1995). *Textbook of Basic Nursing* (6th ed.). Philadelphia, PA: Lippincott.

Saskatchewan Registered Nurses Association. (1998). *Standards and Foundation Competencies for the Practice of Registered Nurses*, Draft #2. Regina, SK: Author.

Schultz, J. M., & Videbeck, S. D. (1998). *Lippincott's Manual of Psychiatric Nursing Care Plans* (5th ed.). Philadelphia, PA: Lippincott-Raven.

Shapiro, P. J. (1995). *Basic Maternal Pediatric Nursing*. Albany, NY: Delmar Publishers Inc.

Skidmore-Roth, L. (1997). *1997 Mosby's Nursing Drug Reference*. Toronto, ON: Mosby.

Smeltzer, S. C., & Bare, B. G. (1996). *Brunner and Suddarth's Textbook of Medical-Surgical Nursing* (7th ed.). Philadelphia, PA: Lippincott.

Smith, C. M., & Maurer, F. A. (1995). *Community Health Nursing*. Philadelphia, PA: Saunders.

Spradley, B. W., & Allender, J. A. (1996). *Community Health Nursing: Concepts and Practices* (4th ed.). Philadelphia, PA: Lippincott.

Springhouse. (1998). *Nursing 98 Drug Handbook*. Philadelphia, PA: Author.

Stackhouse, J. C. (1998). *Into the Community: Nursing in Ambulatory and Home Care*. Philadelphia, PA: Lippincott.

Stanhope, M., & Lancaster, J. (1996). *Community Health Nursing: Concepts and Practices* (4th ed.). St. Louis, MO: Mosby.

Stewart, M. J. (1995). *Community Nursing: Promoting Canadians' Health*. Toronto, ON: Saunders.

Stuart, G. W., & Laraia, M. T. (1998). *Principles and Practice of Psychiatric Nursing* (6th ed.). St. Louis, MO: Mosby.

Taylor, C., Lillis, C., & LeMone, P. (1997). *Fundamentals of Nursing: The Art and Science of Nursing Care* (3rd ed.). Philadelphia, PA: Lippincott.

Thelan, L. A., Urden, L. D., Lough, M. E., & Stacy, K. M. (1998). *Critical Care Nursing: Diagnosis and Management* (3rd ed.). St. Louis, MO: Mosby.

Thompson, E. D. (1995). *Introduction to Maternity and Pediatric Nursing* (2nd ed.). Philadelphia, PA: Saunders.

Tierney, L. M., McPhee, S. J., & Papadakis, M. A. (1998). *Current Medical Diagnosis and Treatment* (37th ed.). Stamford, CT: Appleton & Lange.

Van Servellen, G. M. (1997). *Communication Skills for the Health Care Professional: Concepts and Techniques*. Gaithersburg, MD: Aspen.

Varcarolis, E. M. (1998). *Foundations of Mental Health Nursing* (3rd ed.). Philadelphia, PA: Lippincott.

Varrichio, C., Pierce, M., Walker, C. L., & Ades, T. B. (1997). *A Cancer Source Book for Nurses* (7th ed.). Washington, DC: American Cancer Society.

Vestal Allen, C. 1996. *Nursing Process in Collaborative Practice* (2nd ed.). Stamford, CT: Appleton & Lange.

Weinstein, S. M. (1997). *Plumer's Principles & Practice of Intravenous Therapy* (6th ed.). Philadelphia, PA: Lippincott.

Williams, B. R., & Baer, C. L. (1998). *Essentials of Clinical Pharmacology in Nursing* (3rd ed.). Philadelphia, PA: Springhouse.

Williams, S. R. (1995). *Basic Nutrition and Diet Therapy* (10th ed.). St. Louis, MO: Mosby.

Wong, D. L. (1999). *Whaley & Wong's Nursing Care of Infants and Children* (6th ed.), St. Louis, MO: Mosby.

Wong, D. L. (1995). *Whaley & Wong's Nursing Care of Infants and Children* (5th ed.). St. Louis, MO: Mosby.

World Health Organization. (1996). *WHO Constitution*. Geneva: Author.

Appendices
A B C

Appendix A: The RN Exam Competencies

Assumptions

In developing the set of competencies for the RN Exam, a number of assumptions were made:

- The RN Exam competencies are directed toward the practice of the entry-level registered nurse in Canada.

- The entry-level registered nurse is prepared to practise safely and effectively along the continuum of care in situations of health and illness across the client's life cycle.

- The term client is defined as the individual, family, group, population, community that accesses the services of an entry-level registered nurse.

- Health is broader than the provision of health care, embracing health promotion, disease prevention and the underlying determinants of health in the context of healthy public policy and healthy communities (Health Action Lobby [HEAL], 1996).

- The relationship between a nurse and a client is a partnership based on the recognition that clients are able to make decisions about their health situation and are partners in the decision-making process. The extent to which a client participates is determined by the client's health status, willingness, expectations, and readiness to participate (Saskatchewan Registered Nurses Association, 1998).

- The RN Exam competencies are measured within the context of health situations. These situations represent current health trends and may be forecast by determinants of health (e.g., education, environment, morbidity and mortality rates), anticipated maturational process, and the availability of health care services.

- The practice environment of the entry-level registered nurse can be any setting or circumstance within which nursing is practised. It includes, but is not limited to, the site of activity (e.g., institutions, clinics, homes, communities), programs designed to address client health, and resources available to the client and nurse.

- Registered nurses strive to assist clients to resolve health problems or to improve their health situation through a problem-solving approach. The problem-solving approach is a continuous systematic method of assessing human responses to health situations and developing plans aimed at achieving desired health outcomes. In applying the problem-solving approach, nurses use several competencies including critical thinking, decision-making, interpersonal skills, and technical skills (Carol Vestal Allen, 1996).

- Nursing practice is grounded in the values espoused by the Canadian Nurses Association's *Code of Ethics for Registered Nurses* (1997); these values are reflected throughout the competencies.

- The entry-level registered nurse is prepared to practise autonomously and collaboratively in stable situations, and collaboratively, in consultation, or under direction in unstable situations.

- The entry-level registered nurse is prepared to function in a technological work environment. Clinical technology continues to evolve and significantly affects nursing practice.

Competencies

1. Nurse-Client Relationship

The nurse-client relationship is a relationship that is therapeutic and is established to meet the health needs of clients. The relationship is based on trust, respect, and knowledge, and involves interactions that are purposeful and focused on working with clients to maximize client-identified health status outcomes.

The nurse:

NCR-1	establishes a professional relationship with the client (e.g., interprets the nursing role with respect to availability, accessibility, responsibility and limitations; responds to client's concerns; identifies self by name and role).	2
NCR-2	uses therapeutic communication techniques with the client (e.g., identification of communication barriers; use of other approaches to communicate when barriers exist; use of appropriate means to communicate with an unconscious client).	1
NCR-3	identifies effects of own values and assumptions on interactions with clients.	2
NCR-4	applies the principles of a helping relationship (e.g., openness, non-judgmental attitude, active listening).	2
NCR-5	demonstrates consideration for client diversity (e.g., sexual orientation, childbirth practices, dietary differences, gender, beliefs, values, spirituality).	1
NCR-6	provides culturally-sensitive care when working with the client (e.g., openness, sensitivity, recognizing the culturally based health practices and values).	2
NCR-7	discerns when client's health practices can be accommodated or modified (e.g., methods of child discipline, alcohol and drug use).	1
NCR-8	collaborates with the client in planning and evaluating care (e.g., validates data with clients; reviews and measures health care outcomes; determines the client's satisfaction with process and outcome of care).	2
NCR-9	facilitates the client's participation in all aspects of care (i.e., fosters an environment that encourages questioning, exchange of information, and a creative approach to care).	2
NCR-10	selects interventions that are consistent with the client's identified concerns and priorities.	1

NCR-11	supports the informed choice of the client to make decisions regarding care.	1
NCR-12	considers the client's existing resources throughout the plan of care (e.g., financial restrictions, transportation, social network, physical ability).	1
NCR-13	obtains client's consent prior to involving others in care.	2
NCR-14	applies principles of effective group processes.	2
NCR-15	maintains a caring environment that assists the client in achieving health outcomes.	2

2. Health Promotion

Health promotion is a focus of care motivated by the desire to enable clients to increase control over and improve their well-being, thereby actualizing client health potential. It includes encouraging healthy lifestyles, creating supportive environments for health, strengthening community action, reorienting health services and building healthy public policy.

The nurse:

HP-1	identifies determinants of health that are pertinent to the client and the situation (e.g., income, social status, education, employment, work conditions).	2
HP-2	collaborates with the client to develop and establish health promotion priorities.	2
HP-3	assists the client in understanding the link between health promotion strategies and health outcomes (e.g., possible risk and benefits).	1
HP-4	supports the client's choice to use alternate therapies (e.g., aromatherapy, acupressure, therapeutic touch, nutritional supplements, diets).	2
HP-5	incorporates cultural practices in health promotion activities.	1
HP-6	encourages the client to seek out groups for mutual aid, support, and community action.	2
HP-7	coordinates activities with client and others to facilitate continuity of care (e.g., nutrition program for pregnant women, seniors walking group).	2
HP-8	develops learning plans in collaboration with the client.	2
HP-9	identifies areas for health promotion (e.g., healthy public policy, scent-free environment, latex-free environment).	2

HP-10	assesses the learning needs of the client (e.g., community assessment).	2
HP-11	selects appropriate medium and learning strategies to meet client's learning needs and available resources.	2
HP-12	encourages the client to assume ownership of health promotion plan (e.g., self-managed support groups, self-care activities).	1
HP-13	incorporates research findings in health promotion activities (e.g., health trends and statistics, population demographics).	2
HP-14	assists the client in implementing learning plans.	2
HP-15	verifies client's comprehension of essential information and skills.	2
HP-16	verifies client's ability to apply essential information and skills.	2
HP-17	provides evidence-based health-related information to the client.	2
HP-18	uses principles of teaching/learning in health promotion (e.g., assesses readiness to learn, identifies strategies for change, establishes creative environment conducive to learning).	1
HP-19	involves key stakeholders in health promotion activities (e.g., community leaders, public and private sector organizations, special interest groups).	2
HP-20	supports the client through developmental transitions (e.g., puberty, menopause, new community).	2
HP-21	supports the client in role change (e.g., parenting, retirement, economic issues).	2
HP-22	teaches about family planning.	2
HP-23	promotes healthy environment with client (e.g., lobbying, health fairs, anti-smoking campaign, sanitation, ergonomics).	2
HP-24	promotes health habits related to physical activity/exercise.	2
HP-25	promotes the use of healthy coping strategies to deal with life events.	2
HP-26	promotes health habits related to nutrition (e.g., breastfeeding, adherence to Canada's Food Guide).	1

HP-27	promotes balance between rest/sleep and activity (e.g., good sleep habits, removing stimuli).	2
HP-28	promotes stress reduction strategies (e.g., relaxation techniques, recreational activities).	2
HP-29	promotes health practices related to hygiene (e.g., hand washing, waste disposal).	1
HP-30	promotes healthy sexuality (e.g., gender identity, maturational changes, reducing discrimination).	1
HP-31	promotes safe sexual practices.	2

3. Illness/Injury Prevention

Illness/injury prevention is a focus of care motivated by the desire to enable clients to avoid illness and injury. It includes risk factor reduction, screening and early detection of illness, communicable disease control and environmental health and safety.

The nurse:

IIP-1	uses data collection techniques pertinent to the client and the situation (e.g., selected screening tests, risk assessment scales, measuring and monitoring).	2
IIP-2	identifies actual or potential health problems/risk factors.	2
IIP-3	identifies actual or potential safety risks to the client (e.g., incidents and accidents, environmental pollution, mechanical equipment, domestic violence).	2
IIP-4	incorporates research findings about health risks and risk reduction into plan of care.	2
IIP-5	collaborates with clients to reduce complex health risks into manageable components.	2
IIP-6	collaborates with client to prioritize needs and develop risk prevention strategies.	2
IIP-7	reduces the risk of disease transmission (e.g., adheres to reporting protocols, uses universal precautions, encourages needle exchange program).	1
IIP-8	minimizes sensory overload (e.g., reducing noise, facilitating continuity of health care delivery, preventing information overload).	2
IIP-9	employs safety measures to prevent client injury (e.g., accessibility of a call bell, supervision, non-violent crisis intervention, suicide prevention).	2

IIP-10	encourages the client's use of safety measures to prevent injury (e.g., seat belts, bicycle helmets, "safe grad program," smoke alarms).	2
IIP-11	helps the client to understand preventable health problems or issues and their consequences.	1
IIP-12	implements strategies to prevent communicable diseases (e.g., immunization).	2
IIP-13	implements strategies to prevent domestic violence, abuse, and neglect (e.g., using screening tools, providing information).	2
IIP-14	implements strategies related to the prevention/early detection of prevalent diseases (e.g., cardiovascular, cancer, diabetes, mental illness).	2
IIP-15	implements strategies related to the prevention of addictive behaviours (e.g., smoking, alcohol abuse, illicit drug use).	2
IIP-16	implements strategies to minimize the risk of mental health problems (e.g., stress management, support groups).	2
IIP-17	implements preventive strategies related to the safe use of medication (e.g., overuse of antibiotics, polypharmacy).	2
IIP-18	implements preventive strategies related to environmental safety (e.g., fire safety, smoke detectors, playground safety).	2
IIP-19	implements preventive strategies related to workplace safety (e.g., WHMIS, needle stick injury prevention, back injury prevention).	2
IIP-20	evaluates the effectiveness of preventive measures with the client.	2
IIP-21	employs safety measures to protect self from injury (e.g., latex sensitivity protocols, used needle disposal, needleless systems).	1
IIP-22	employs safety measures to protect self from potentially abusive situations in the work environment.	2

4. Curative/Supportive Care

The focus of curative/supportive care is to help clients deal with responses associated with illness or health issues/problems, along with activities designed to support clients as they resolve their health problems or participate in palliative care.

The nurse:

CSC-1	uses appropriate techniques for data collection (e.g., observation, auscultation, palpation, percussion, inspection, selected screening tests, interview, consultation, focus group, measuring and monitoring).	1
CSC-2	collects data about various dimensions of the client (e.g., vital signs, circulatory and respiratory status, lifestyle factors, sensory deficits, level of consciousness, family environment, housing, work milieu, community).	1
CSC-3	collects data from a range of appropriate sources (e.g., the client, previous and current health records/nursing care plans, family members/significant persons/ substitute decision maker, census data, and epidemiological data).	1
CSC-4	adapts the assessment to the client's situation (e.g., growth and development stage).	1
CSC-5	validates the data with the client and/or appropriate sources.	1
CSC-6	establishes relationships between and among the various data collected (e.g., determines relationship between health assessment and laboratory values).	2
CSC-7	interprets data within the context of scientific knowledge and norms (e.g., takes the analyzed data and determines that the client's colour, blood gas report and statement of dyspnea are not normal and that a problem exists with the respiratory system).	1
CSC-8	identifies actual and potential health problems.	1
CSC-9	develops the plan of care (e.g., setting priorities, establishing target dates, identifying and prioritizing nursing interventions).	2
CSC-10	documents the plan of care.	1
CSC-11	selects interventions that are consistent with the priority of the health situation.	2
CSC-12	modifies interventions to suit the client's situation by selecting interventions that are consistent with the client's identified concerns and priorities.	2

CSC-13	selects appropriate technology in accordance with available resources and client needs (e.g., blood pressure monitor, infusion pump).	2
CSC-14	supports the client's participation in the implementation of plan of care (e.g., administration of insulin, home IV and TPN programs, self-care groups).	2
CSC-15	helps the client understand the interventions and their relationship to expected outcomes (e.g., possible risk, discomforts, inconveniences, costs).	2
CSC-16	uses principles of teaching and learning with the client receiving curative/ supportive care.	1
CSC-17	facilitates appropriate and timely responses of the health team members to client care needs.	2
CSC-18	coordinates activities with the client and others to promote continuity of care.	2
CSC-19	prepares the client for diagnostic procedures and treatments using appropriate resources (e.g., explanation, information, tests, obtaining specimens from the client).	2
CSC-20	provides client care throughout the perioperative experience (i.e., pre- and postoperative care).	1
CSC-21	promotes optimal ventilation and respiration (e.g., positioning, deep breathing and coughing exercises, oxygen therapy).	2
CSC-22	ensures ventilation and respiration when breathing is impaired (e.g., performs oral or nasal suctioning, performs cardiopulmonary resuscitation).	2
CSC-23	promotes circulation (e.g., active or passive exercises, positioning, mobilization, cast care).	2
CSC-24	monitors fluid balance (e.g., weight, hemodynamic measurement, measuring abdominal girth).	2
CSC-25	promotes adequate fluid intake.	2
CSC-26	relates nutritional needs to physiological conditions (e.g., burns, inflammatory bowel disease).	1
CSC-27	manages nutritional access devices (e.g., TPN, nasogastric tube).	2

CSC-28   promotes urinary elimination in client with compromised system (e.g., irrigating bladder, performing bladder catheterization, pharmacological measures, pushing fluids).   2

CSC-29   promotes bowel elimination in client with compromised system (e.g., enema, rectal tubes, pharmacological and dietary measures).   2

CSC-30   promotes client's correct body alignment (e.g., proper positioning, caring for the client with external immobilizing devices).   2

CSC-31   promotes the tissue integrity of the client (e.g., providing skin and wound care, skin cleansing, wound dressing).   1

CSC-32   promotes comfort by using various measures (e.g., heat and cold application, touch, positioning).   2

CSC-33   promotes sensory stimulation at an appropriate level for the client's health situation (e.g., uses touch with unconscious client, reduces environmental stimuli for the agitated client).   2

CSC-34   intervenes in response to changes observed in the client's condition (i.e., intervenes according to protocols).   1

CSC-35   manages multiple nursing interventions simultaneously (i.e., prioritizes and organizes interventions).   1

CSC-36   communicates to appropriate health team members significant information about the client's condition.   2

CSC-37   modifies plan of care to suit the client's changing situation (i.e., selects interventions that are consistent with the emerging priorities of the health situation and the client's newly identified concerns, priorities and tolerance).   2

CSC-38   calculates medication dosage correctly.   1

CSC-39   determines medication dosage is safe (i.e., considers food-drug interaction, drug-drug interaction, age, weight).   1

CSC-40   administers medication safely and appropriately (i.e., right person, drug, dose, route and time).   1

CSC-41   assesses client's response to drugs (e.g., desired effects, adverse effects, interactions).   1

CSC-42	discerns when a PRN medication is indicated (e.g., analgesics, inhalers, antihypertensives, antianginals, bowel medications).	1
CSC-43	takes appropriate actions when desired responses to medication are not attained.	1
CSC-44	assists client to manage pain with non-pharmacological measures (e.g., applying heat and cold, touch, massage, and visual imagery).	2
CSC-45	assists client to manage pain with pharmaceutical agents (e.g., Patient Controlled Analgesia [PCA]).	2
CSC-46	safely administers blood/blood products.	2
CSC-47	manages venous access devices (e.g., implanted devices, peripheral access).	2
CSC-48	manages drainage tubes and collection devices.	2
CSC-49	inserts and removes nasogastric tubes.	2
CSC-50	maintains established peripheral intravenous therapy.	2
CSC-51	maintains central venous intravenous therapy.	2
CSC-52	applies principles of microbiology and communicable disease transmission as demonstrated through the application of universal precautions.	1
CSC-53	intervenes in a rapidly changing health situation: myocardial infarction.	2
CSC-54	intervenes in a rapidly changing health situation: stroke in evolution.	2
CSC-55	intervenes in a rapidly changing health situation: shock (e.g., hemorrhagic, anaphylactic, neurogenic).	2
CSC-56	intervenes in a rapidly changing health situation: respiratory distress.	2
CSC-57	intervenes in a rapidly changing health situation: labour and delivery.	2
CSC-58	intervenes in a rapidly changing health situation: mental health crisis (e.g., psychotic episode).	2
CSC-59	intervenes in a rapidly changing health situation: trauma (e.g., burns, fractures).	2

CSC-60	evaluates and responds appropriately to status of clients in relation to anticipated outcomes.	2
CSC-61	evaluates the effectiveness of nursing interventions with the client (e.g., learning needs, comparing actual outcomes to anticipated outcomes).	1
CSC-62	prepares the client for discharge.	1
CSC-63	coordinates continuity of care across care settings (e.g., discharge planning, transfer of care).	2
CSC-64	provides supportive care to clients with chronic illnesses (e.g., chronic pain, COPD).	2
CSC-65	performs palliative nursing interventions to meet spiritual needs (e.g., assesses for spiritual distress, provides time for prayer/meditation).	2
CSC-66	performs palliative nursing interventions to meet physical needs.	2
CSC-67	performs palliative nursing interventions to meet psychosocial needs (e.g., grief work).	2
CSC-68	provides care that is sensitive to clients experiencing loss (e.g., death, amputation, natural disaster).	1
CSC-69	provides supportive care throughout the dying process (e.g., symptoms control, family counselling, advocacy).	2

5. Rehabilitative Care

The focus of rehabilitative care is to assist clients with a physical or psychosocial disabling injury or illness to achieve maximum functioning or independence. This includes counselling, support, retraining and education, and environmental modifications.

The nurse:

RC-1	facilitates continuity and consistency of care in the approach used by all members of the health care team.	2
RC-2	individualizes care to accommodate client's deficits in sensory and cognitive functions.	2
RC-3	begins rehabilitative measures at the earliest opportunity.	2
RC-4	provides nursing care to prevent the development of complications that can impede recovery (e.g., turning immobile clients q. 2h., early intervention of first and last chest infection detected with CHF/COPD).	1

RC-5   promotes the client's positive self-concept (e.g., supporting cultural and spiritual   I
          preferences, validating client's strengths, and promoting use of effective coping
          techniques).

RC-6   assists the client in accessing community resources (e.g., self-help groups, geriatric   I
          day programs, respite).

RC-7   supports client to draw on own assets and resources in meeting self-care needs.   2

RC-8   promotes social interaction of client (e.g., encourages and/or creates opportunities   2
          for social participation, encourages development of new interests and support systems).

RC-9   assists the client with prosthetic and mobilizing devices (e.g., walker, brace).   2

RC-10   promotes mobility (e.g., active and passive exercises, range of motion exercises,   I
          early ambulation, activities of daily living).

RC-11   arranges for adaptations in the environment to facilitate the client's development of   2
          independence in activities of daily living (e.g., removal of scatter rugs, keeping
          essential furniture on one level of the house, raised toilet seat, ordering specialized
          equipment such as walker, special utensils).

RC-12   promotes elimination (e.g., ostomy care, bowel and bladder retraining,   2
          self-catheterization).

RC-13   assesses for psychological and psychosocial adaptation (e.g., recognizes depression   2
          and uses resources to assess depression).

RC-14   encourages family and significant others to support the client during the rehabilitation   I
          process.

RC-15   assists client with reintegration into family and community networks (e.g., adaptation   I
          to role changes, physical mobility, self-help groups).

6. Professional Practice

Each nurse is accountable to clients for practising within professional, legal, and ethical standards. This includes applying quality improvement principles, using evidence-based knowledge and critical thinking, establishing collaborative partnerships, coordinating care, monitoring practice, enhancing practice, and recognizing and acting on learning needs.

The nurse:

PP-1	practises in a manner consistent with the *Code of Ethics for Registered Nurses* value: health and well-being.	2
PP-2	practises in a manner consistent with the *Code of Ethics for Registered Nurses* value: choice.	2
PP-3	practises in a manner consistent with the *Code of Ethics for Registered Nurses* value: dignity.	2
PP-4	practises in a manner consistent with the *Code of Ethics for Registered Nurses* value: confidentiality.	2
PP-5	practises in a manner consistent with the *Code of Ethics for Registered Nurses* value: fairness.	2
PP-6	practises in a manner consistent with the *Code of Ethics for Registered Nurses* value: accountability.	2
PP-7	practises in a manner consistent with the *Code of Ethics for Registered Nurses* value: practice environment conducive to safe, competent and ethical care.	2
PP-8	practises in a manner consistent with the acts governing nursing practice, the regulatory body's standards for nursing and guidelines for the scope of nursing practice.	2
PP-9	practises in a manner consistent with common law and legislation that directs practice (e.g., criminal code, narcotics control acts).	2
PP-10	exercises professional judgment when following agency procedures, policies, and position requirements.	2
PP-11	exercises professional judgment in the absence of agency procedures, protocols or position statements.	2
PP-12	practises in a manner consistent with professional values, principles of safety and obligation to take action (e.g., intervenes when a policy is unsafe or obsolete; challenges questionable orders, actions or decisions of others).	1

PP-13	advocates for the client or client's representative, especially when the client is unable to advocate for self (e.g., assists client to gain access to quality health care, facilitates and monitors the quality of care, facilitates appropriate and timely responses by health care team members, and challenges questionable decisions).	1
PP-14	maintains clear, concise, accurate and timely records of client care.	1
PP-15	uses appropriate, cost-effective health care resources to provide effective and efficient care (i.e., human, material, technological, financial).	2
PP-16	organizes own workload effectively (e.g., time management, prioritizing, setting time frames).	2
PP-17	identifies an unrealistic workload and seeks assistance as necessary.	2
PP-18	accepts accountability for own actions and decisions when delegating.	2
PP-19	uses evidence-based knowledge from nursing, health sciences and related disciplines in the provision of individualized nursing care (e.g., to plan care, to select nursing interventions).	1
PP-20	recognizes limitations of own competence and seeks assistance when necessary.	2
PP-21	delegates health care activities to others consistent with levels of expertise, education, job description/agency policy, and client needs.	2
PP-22	evaluates the outcomes of delegated health care activities.	1
PP-23	builds partnerships with nursing and members of the health care team to provide health services.	2
PP-24	clarifies the nurse's role and responsibilities to other health care team members (e.g., with regulated and unregulated health care providers).	1
PP-25	demonstrates respect for colleagues (e.g., respect for unique and shared competencies of health care team members).	2
PP-26	maintains effective communication with the health care team.	2
PP-27	provides constructive feedback to colleagues (e.g., about client care, peer assessment).	1
PP-28	uses conflict resolution skills to facilitate health care team interactions.	1

PP-29   reports unsafe practice of nursing colleagues and other members of the health care   2
         team to the appropriate authority.

PP-30   uses established communication protocols within the health care agency, across   2
         agencies, health system and community.

PP-31   participates in planning, implementing and evaluating changes that affect nursing   2
         practice, client care, and the practice environment.

Appendix B

To obtain information on writing the Canadian Registered Nurse Examination, contact the regulatory authority for your province or territory. The following is the contact information for the jurisdictions that use the RN Exam.

**Alberta Association of
Registered Nurses**
11620 – 168th Street
Edmonton AB T5M 4A6

Tel: (780) 453-0506
Fax: (780) 452-3276
Email: aarn@nurses.ab.ca
Web: www.nurses.ab.ca

**Manitoba Association of
Registered Nurses**
647 Broadway Avenue
Winnipeg MB R3C 0X2

Tel: (204) 774-3477
Fax: (204) 775-6052
Email: marn@marn.mb.ca
Web: www.marn.mb.ca

**Registered Nurses Association
of British Columbia**
2855 Arbutus Street
Vancouver BC V6J 3Y8

Tel: (604) 736-7331
Fax: (604) 738-2272
Web: www.rnabc.bc.ca

**Association of Nurses of
Prince Edward Island**
17 Pownal Street
Charlottetown PE C1A 7M5

Tel: (902) 368-3764
Fax: (902) 628-1430
Web: www.anpei@pei.sympatico.ca

**Northwest Territories Registered
Nurses Association**
P.O. Box 2757
Yellowknife NT X1A 2R1

Tel: (867) 873-2745
Fax: (867) 873-2336
Email: nwtrna@internorth.com
Web: http://users.internorth.com/~nwtrna/

**Registered Nurses' Association
of Nova Scotia**
Suite 600, Barrington Tower
Scotia Square, 1894 Barrington St
Halifax NS B3J 2A8

Tel: (902) 491-9744
Fax: (902) 491-9510
Email: info@rnans.ns.ca
Web: www.rnans.ns.ca

**Association of Registered
Nurses of Newfoundland and Labrador**
P.O. Box 6116
55 Military Rd.
St. John's NF A1C 5X8

Tel: (709) 753-6040
Fax: (709) 753-4940
Email: arnn@nf.sympatico.ca
Web: www.arnn.nf.ca

**Nurses Association of New Brunswick/
Association des infirmières et infirmiers
du Nouveau-Brunswick**
165 Regent Street
Fredericton NB E3B 3W5

Tel: (506) 458-8731
Fax: (506) 459-2838
Email: nanb@nanb.nb.ca
Web: www.nanb.nb.ca

Saskatchewan Registered Nurses' Association
2066 Retallack Street
Regina SK S4T 7X5

Tel: (306) 757-4643
Fax: (306) 525-0849
Email: srna@sasknet.sk.ca
Web: www.srna.org

College of Nurses of Ontario
101 Davenport Road
Toronto ON M5R 3P1

Tel: (416) 928-0900
Fax: (416) 928-6507
Email: cno@cnomail.org
Web: www.cno.org

Yukon Registered Nurses Association
Suite 14, 1114 – 1 Avenue
Whitehorse YK Y1A 1A3

Tel: (867) 667-4062
Fax: (867) 668-5123
Email: yrna@yukon.net

Abbreviations Used in the Practice Exam

The abbreviations used in the Practice Exam are defined as follows:

BP	—	blood pressure	mg	—	milligram(s)
b.i.d.	—	twice daily	ml	—	millilitre(s)
°C	—	degrees Celsius	mmHg	—	millimetres mercury
cm	—	centimetre(s)	min	—	minute(s)
g	—	gram	P	—	pulse
gtt	—	drops	p.o.	—	orally
h	—	hour	p.r.n.	—	as needed
IM	—	intramuscular	q.i.d.	—	4 times daily
IV	—	intravenous	q. 8h.	—	every 8 hours
kg	—	kilogram(s)	stat.	—	immediately
L	—	litre(s)	T	—	temperature
mEq	—	milliequivalent	t.i.d.	—	3 times daily

Additional materials

Performance Profile Tally Sheet

Table 1: Competency Category

CATEGORY	TOTAL INCORRECT	% INCORRECT
N-CR	÷ 21 X 100 =	%
HP	÷ 42 X 100 =	%
I/IP	÷ 28 X 100 =	%
C/SC	÷ 112 X 100 =	%
RC	÷ 24 X 100 =	%
PP	÷ 33 X 100 =	%

Table 2: Taxonomic Level

CATEGORY	TOTAL INCORRECT	% INCORRECT
K/C	÷ 66 X 100 =	%
APP	÷ 130 X 100 =	%
CT	÷ 53 X 100 =	%
AD	÷ 11 X 100 =	%

Competency Categories

N-CR – Nurse-Client Relationship
HP – Health Promotion
I/IP – Illness/Injury Prevention
C/SC – Curative/Supportive Care
RC – Rehabilitative Care
PP – Professional Practice

Taxonomic Level

K/C – Knowledge/Comprehension
APP – Application
CT – Critical Thinking
AD – Affective Domain

Performance Profile Tally Sheet

Table 3: Client Type

CATEGORY	TOTAL INCORRECT	% INCORRECT
I	÷ 169 X 100 =	%
F	÷ 53 X 100 =	%
G/P/C	÷ 38 X 100 =	%

Table 4: Age Group

CATEGORY	TOTAL INCORRECT	% INCORRECT
0-18	÷ 66 X 100 =	%
19-64	÷ 117 X 100 =	%
65-79	÷ 53 X 100 =	%
80+	÷ 13 X 100 =	%
NA	÷ 11 X 100 =	%

Client Type

I   –   Individuals
F   –   Families
G/P/C   –   Groups, Populations, Communities

Age Group

0-18   –   Child/adolescent
19-64   –   Adult
65-79   –   Older Adult
80+   –   Adult of Advanced Age
NA   –   Not Applicable

Performance Profile Chart

Table 1: Competency Category

% OF INCORRECT ANSWERS

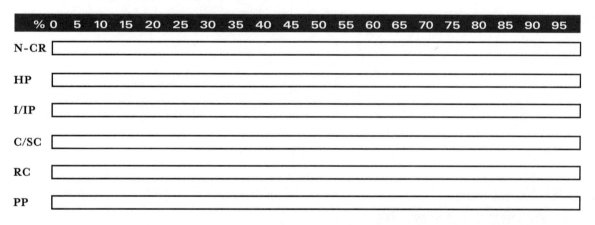

%	0	5	10	15	20	25	30	35	40	45	50	55	60	65	70	75	80	85	90	95
N-CR																				
HP																				
I/IP																				
C/SC																				
RC																				
PP																				

Table 2: Taxonomic Level

% OF INCORRECT ANSWERS

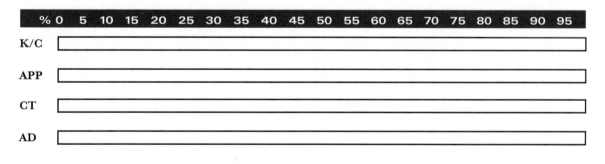

%	0	5	10	15	20	25	30	35	40	45	50	55	60	65	70	75	80	85	90	95
K/C																				
APP																				
CT																				
AD																				

Competency Categories

N-CR	–	Nurse-Client Relationship
HP	–	Health Promotion
I/IP	–	Illness/Injury Prevention
C/SC	–	Curative/Supportive Care
RC	–	Rehabilitative Care
PP	–	Professional Practice

Taxonomic Level

K/C	–	Knowledge/Comprehension
APP	–	Application
CT	–	Critical Thinking
AD	–	Affective Domain

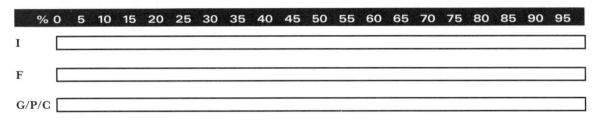

Performance Profile Chart

Table 3: Client Type

% OF INCORRECT ANSWERS

%	0	5	10	15	20	25	30	35	40	45	50	55	60	65	70	75	80	85	90	95

I

F

G/P/C

Table 4: Age Group

% OF INCORRECT ANSWERS

%	0	5	10	15	20	25	30	35	40	45	50	55	60	65	70	75	80	85	90	95

0-18

19-64

65-79

80+

NA

Client Type

I   –   Individuals
F   –   Families
G/P/C   –   Groups, Populations, Communities

Age Group

0-18   –   Child/adolescent
19-64 –   Adult
65-79 –   Older Adult
80+   –   Adult of Advanced Age
NA   –   Not Applicable